DATE DUE

THE
INORGANIC CHEMISTRY
OF NITROGEN

THE PHYSICAL INORGANIC CHEMISTRY SERIES

Robert A. Plane and Michell J. Sienko, Editors

Physical Inorganic Chemistry   *M. J. Sienko and R. A. Plane*
                                     (Cornell)

Boron Hydrides   *W. N. Lipscomb (Harvard)*

Metal Ions in Aqueous Solution   *J. P. Hunt (Washington State)*

Inorganic Chemistry of Nitrogen *W. L. Jolly (Berkeley)*

Inorganic Reaction Mechanisms   *J. O. Edwards (Brown)*

THE

INORGANIC CHEMISTRY

OF NITROGEN

WILLIAM L. JOLLY

University of California, Berkeley

W. A. BENJAMIN, INC.

1964   New York   Amsterdam

THE INORGANIC CHEMISTRY OF NITROGEN

Library of Congress Catalog Card Number 63-19981
Manufactured in the United States of America

*Final manuscript was received on March 20, 1963;
this volume was published on January 30, 1964*

Feb. 1968

*The publisher is pleased to acknowledge the assistance
of Oren Hunt, who produced the illustrations, and
William Prokos, who designed the dust jacket*

W. A. BENJAMIN, INC.
New York, New York

Editors' Foreword

In recent years few fields of chemistry have expanded at a rate to match that of inorganic chemistry. Aside from the stimulus afforded by the demand for new materials, a primary cause for the resurgence has been the application of physics and physical chemistry concepts to inorganic problems. As a result, both researchers active in the field and students entering the field need to become as thoroughly familiar with physical concepts as with descriptive information. However, there is presently no single point of view sufficiently general to organize the entire discipline. Instead, various points of view have arisen corresponding to the most powerful methods of attack in each research area. The synthesis of these different points of view constitutes the present series of monographs. Each monograph is contributed by an inorganic chemist active in a particular research area and reflects the methods of approach characteristic to that area. The operational procedure has been to invite able scientists to write where their interests lead them.

The series fulfills several functions. Through flexible selection of several of the monographs to supplement the introductory volume, it can be used as a textbook for an advanced inorganic chemistry course that makes full use of physical chemistry prerequisites. As a series in total, it is a reference treatise of inorganic chemistry systematized by physical principles.   Finally, each monograph by itself represents a specialist's introduction to a specific research field.

It is hoped that the authors contributing to this series have succeeded in directing attention to unsolved problems and that their efforts will be repaid by continued research advances in inorganic chemistry.

M. J. SIENKO
R. A. PLANE

Ithaca, New York
February 1963

Preface

Among the innumerable compounds of nitrogen, one finds a wide variety of molecular structures and properties. Many of these compounds have practical importance. A few important categories are: biochemically significant compounds (such as proteins, porphyrins, alkaloids, vitamins, drugs, and fertilizers), nitrogen oxides (important in air pollution, atmospheric physics, and astrophysics), explosives (mostly nitro compounds), fuels (substituted hydrazines), and plastics (e.g., Nylon).

Even if there were no useful nitrogen compounds, chemists would still find nitrogen chemistry quite fascinating. This fascination is attributable to the fact that the chemical reactions of nitrogen compounds are seldom thermodynamically controlled. Therefore it is possible to prepare compounds that are thermodynamically unstable but that decompose at a negligible rate. In this respect we are quite fortunate, because almost all the compounds mentioned above are thermodynamically unstable. Whenever a nitrogen compound can react to form several alternative products, it is quite commonly observed that the most thermodynamically stable product does not form at all, or that several products form simultaneously. For this reason, nitrogen compounds form a happy hunting ground for kineticists, who attempt to unravel and systematize the mechanisms of the reactions.

WILLIAM L. JOLLY

Berkeley, California
October 1963

Contents

ix

I

The Unique Features of
Nitrogen

The unique features of nitrogen chemistry may be emphasized by comparing nitrogen with the three elements that are adjacent to it in the periodic table: carbon, phosphorus, and oxygen.

1-1 COMPARISON WITH CARBON

Whereas carbon atoms readily link together to form long chains (as in hydrocarbons), very few nitrogen compounds contain chains of more than two consecutive nitrogen atoms. This striking difference between carbon and nitrogen is a manifestation of the very weak N—N single bond, which is probably a consequence of the repulsion of the lone-pair electrons on the nitrogen atoms.

In the elementary state, carbon is a giant molecule (graphite or diamond), whereas elementary nitrogen exists as a diatomic molecule. Of course, carbon cannot form a stable diatomic molecule $C\equiv C$ because of the extreme electron repulsion that would exist in the quadruple bond. Or to put it another way, the tetrahedrally directed valences of carbon prohibit the formation of a quadruple bond.[1]

The simple hydrides methane and ammonia differ enormously in their physical and chemical properties. Methane forms an unassociated, low-boiling liquid and is a rather chemically inert material. Ammonia forms an associated, relatively high-boiling liquid and is a reactive, basic material. These differences are again due to the lone pair of electrons on the nitrogen atom that causes the ammonia molecule to have an electric dipole moment in contrast to the completely symmetric methane molecule.

1-2 COMPARISON WITH PHOSPHORUS

The single-bonded structures of white and red phosphorus contrast with the triple-bonded nitrogen molecule. The difference here is probably directly related to the difference in the sizes of the atoms. The lone pair–lone pair repulsion in a P—P bond is not as important as it is in an N—N bond. And because of inadequate overlap of the appropriate p orbitals, the π bonds in P_2 are not as strong as the corresponding bonds in N_2.

Nitrogen in the $+5$ oxidation state forms only one oxy-acid, HNO_3. On the other hand, phosphorus forms a whole series of phosphates in which each phosphorus atom is surrounded by four oxygen atoms. Phosphorus forms the compounds PCl_5 and PF_5 and the ion PF_6^-, whereas nitrogen forms no analogous species.

These differences can largely be ascribed to the relative sizes of the phosphorus and nitrogen atoms. The nitrogen atom is apparently too small to coordinate more than three oxygen atoms or fluorine atoms. In order to maintain an octet of electrons around the nitrogen atom, we must ascribe double-bond character to the N—O bonds in HNO_3 and NO_3^-. The $3d$ orbitals of phosphorus are of only slightly higher energy level than the $3s$ and $3p$ orbitals and are probably involved in the bonding of the phosphorus compounds mentioned above. Of course, nitrogen has no comparable $2d$ orbitals available for bonding.

Phosphine, PH_3, is a much weaker base than ammonia and has H—P—H bond angles of $93°$ in contrast to ammonia's H—N—H

---

[1] The C_2 gaseous molecule has a double bond and is extremely unstable with respect to graphite.

bond angles of 106° 47'. Both of these features correspond to a greater degree of *s* character in the lone pair of phosphine (and consequently more *p* character in the bonds to hydrogen), an effect which may again be ascribed to the larger size of phosphorus compared to that of nitrogen.

The four pairs of electrons (three bonding pairs and one lone pair) around the nitrogen atom in ammonia are quite crowded, and although there is appreciable repulsion between the lone pair and the bonding pairs, the H—N—H bond angle cannot decrease far below the tetrahedral value because of the repulsion between bonding pairs that sets in at lower bond angles. In phosphine, however, repulsion among the bonding pairs of electrons becomes important only at much smaller bond angles. The bond angles in phosphine, arsine, and stibene are all slightly greater than 90° and correspond to the use of practically pure *p* orbitals in bonding.

1-3 COMPARISON WITH OXYGEN

Because of its smaller size and higher nuclear charge, oxygen is more electronegative than nitrogen. Thus although water, alcohols, and ethers have two lone pairs of electrons on their oxygen atoms in contrast to the single lone pair in ammonia and amines, ammonia and amines are much stronger bases than the corresponding oxygen compounds.[2]

The greater electronegativity of oxygen perhaps also explains why water is a much more hydrogen-bonded liquid than is liquid ammonia. The hydrogen ion in water migrates by a very rapid mechanism involving a shift of hydrogen bonds. In ammonia, the corresponding process involves the diffusion of ammonium ions and is a much slower process.

REFERENCES

L. Pauling, *The Nature of the Chemical Bond*, 3d ed., Cornell University Press, Ithaca, N.Y., 1960.
C. A. Coulson, *Valence*, 2d ed., Oxford University Press, London, 1961.
H. A. Bent, " Distribution of atomic *s* character in molecules and its chemical implications," *J. Chem. Educ.*, **37**, 616 (1960).
R. J. Gillespie, " Bond angles and spatial correlation of electrons," *J. Am. Chem. Soc.*, **82**, 5978 (1960).

[2] For similar reasons the methide ion CH_3^- is a stronger base than the amide ion NH_2^-.

2

Elementary Nitrogen

2-1 SOURCES AND PREPARATION

Dry air contains nitrogen to the extent of 78.09 per cent by volume. Practically all nitrogen of commerce is produced by the liquefaction and fractional distillation of air. The nitrogen in ordinary cylinders of compressed nitrogen usually has a guaranteed purity of 99.7 per cent and contains about 0.1 mole per cent of oxygen. However, specially purified nitrogen containing less than 0.0005 mole per cent of oxygen and hydrogen, less than 0.005 mole per cent of argon, and less than 0.0001 mole per cent of water is available in cylinders.

Oxygen (in small amounts) may be conveniently removed from nitrogen by passing the gas through either a tube containing copper wool heated to about 400° or a gas-washing bottle containing chromous chloride solution.[1] Residual water may be removed by passing the gas through an efficient trap cooled with

---

[1] When the scale letter is not supplied, a temperature should be taken as measured in degrees centigrade.

liquid nitrogen or through a tube containing a desiccant such as magnesium perchlorate or phosphorus pentoxide.

A variety of methods have been used to prepare nitrogen gas in the laboratory. Hot aqueous solutions of ammonium nitrite decompose to give nitrogen according to the reaction

$$NH_4^+ + NO_2^- \rightarrow N_2 + 2H_2O$$

Small amounts of nitric oxide and nitric acid are also formed, and they must be removed by suitable absorbents. Ammonium dichromate decomposes on heating to give nitrogen:

$$(NH_4)_2Cr_2O_7 \rightarrow N_2 + Cr_2O_3 + 4H_2O$$

When ammonia is passed into bromine water, the principal reaction is the oxidation of ammonia to nitrogen:

$$8NH_3 + 3Br_2 \rightarrow N_2 + 6NH_4^+ + 6Br^-$$

Nitrogen may be prepared by the high-temperature reaction between ammonia and cupric oxide:

$$2NH_3 + 3CuO \rightarrow N_2 + 3H_2O + 3Cu$$

Extremely pure nitrogen may be prepared by the careful thermal decomposition of sodium azide:

$$2NaN_3 \rightarrow 2Na + 3N_2$$

2-2 BONDING

The bonding in molecular nitrogen may be satisfactorily explained in terms of the Lewis octet theory by formulas such as the following:

$$:N:::N: \quad \text{or} \quad :N\equiv N:$$

It is obvious that six of the valence electrons are engaged in bonding and that the other four valence electrons exist as lone pairs. A similar conclusion is reached by putting electrons into the molecular orbitals, which may be thought of as being formed from the overlap of atomic orbitals of the nitrogen atoms. There are many ways in which we may imagine these molecular orbitals being formed. Three ways are described below; each gives a satisfactory picture of the bonding in molecular nitrogen.

First, let us imagine that the s and three p orbitals of each nitrogen atom are so hybridized that all four orbitals are equivalent and are directed toward the corners of a regular tetrahedron. If, as shown in Figure 2-1, three orbitals of one atom are made to overlap three orbitals of the other atom, three equivalent bonding molecular orbitals will form, with the lone pairs directed away from the molecule on the molecular axis.

Second, let us imagine that the *s* and a *p* orbital of each nitrogen atom are hybridized to two equivalent orbitals directed at 180° from the atom. The two remaining *p* orbitals will then be in a plane perpendicular to the axis of the *sp* hybrid orbitals. If, as shown in Figure 2-2, the atoms approach each other along an axis common to the *sp* hybrid orbitals, a bonding molecular orbital will form by the overlap of an *sp* hybrid orbital from each atom and two bonding molecular orbitals by the overlap of the *p* orbitals perpendicular to the molecular axis. Again the lone pairs will be directed away from the molecule that lies on the molecular axis.

Third, consider two nitrogen atoms each of which has one of its *p* orbitals on a common axis passing through the nuclei (see Figure 2-3). As these atoms approach one another, a σ-bonding molecular orbital will form as the result of the overlap of the two *p* orbitals that point toward each other. Two equivalent π-bonding molecular orbitals will form as the result of the overlap of the *p* orbitals that are perpendicular to the molecular axis. It will be noted that the three bonding orbitals and the two nonbonding

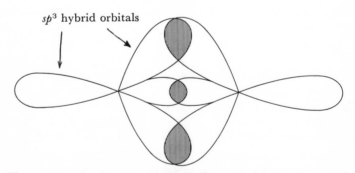

*sp*³ hybrid orbitals

Figure 2-1   *Overlap of three pairs of sp³ hybrid orbitals to form a triple bond. Each lobe represents an sp³ hybrid orbital. This schematic diagram does not show the electron density of the resultant molecule, which has cylindrical symmetry.*

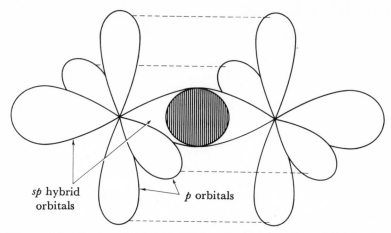

Figure 2-2   *Overlap of sp hydrid orbitals and p orbitals to form a triple bond. This schematic diagram does not show the electron density of the resultant molecule, which has cylindrical symmetry.*

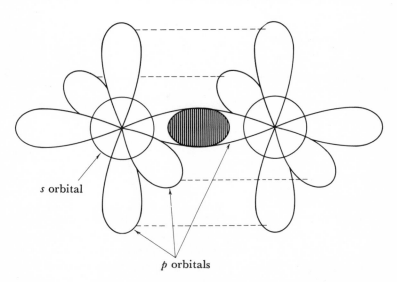

Figure 2-3   *Overlap of three pairs of p orbitals to form a triple bond.   This schematic diagram does not show the electron density of the resultant molecule, which has cylindrical symmetry.*

orbitals will accommodate the 10 valence electrons of the nitrogen atoms. The formation of these molecular orbitals may be expressed by the following equation:

$$2N(1s^2 2s^2 2p^3) \rightarrow N_2(KK(s\sigma)^2(s\sigma^*)^2(p\pi)^4(p\sigma)^2)$$

Here $(s\sigma)$ is bonding and $(s\sigma^*)$ is its antibonding partner; together they are equivalent to two nonbonding orbitals. The $(p\sigma)$ orbital corresponds to the σ bond formed from atomic p orbitals, and $(p\pi)$ corresponds to the two degenerate π bonds formed from atomic p orbitals. This latter description of the bonding and molecular orbital notation is that most commonly used by chemists, although the choice is completely arbitrary.

Because the $(p\pi)$ and $(p\sigma)$ orbitals are completely filled in molecular nitrogen, the ground state is a $^1\Sigma_g^+$ state. The first excited electronic states are

$$N^2(KK(s\sigma)^2(s\sigma^*)^2(p\pi)^4(p\sigma)^1(p\pi^*)^1)$$

corresponding to $^3\pi_g$ and $^1\pi_g$, and

$$N_2(KK(s\sigma)^2(s\sigma^*)^2(p\pi)^3(p\sigma)^2(p\pi^*)^1)$$

corresponding to $^3\Sigma_u^+$ and a series of other states. Complete removal of an electron from N_2 to give N_2^+ requires an energy of 15.576 eV (the ionization potential of N_2). Because this ionization involves the removal of a bonding electron, the bond order decreases from 3 to $2\frac{1}{2}$. Thus the bond distance increases from 1.094 to 1.116 Å and the dissociation energy decreases from 225 to 127 kcal/mole.

2-3 PHYSICAL PROPERTIES

Molecular Constants

In order for a pure rotational spectrum for a molecule to be observed, the molecule must possess a permanent dipole moment. And in order for a vibration-rotation spectrum to be observed, the vibration must produce a change in the dipole moment of the molecule. Since molecular nitrogen is homonuclear, it is obvious that molecular constants cannot be obtained from either microwave or infrared spectra.

In the Raman effect, however, the selection rule for the vibration spectrum states that the motion of the nuclei must produce a change in the polarizability of the molecule. Since the polarizability of molecular nitrogen does change as the length of the bond is altered, the molecule gives a vibrational Raman line along with considerable rotational fine structure. Electronic spectra of nitrogen (corresponding to transitions among the various electronically excited states of N_2) have vibrational and rotational fine structure.

From Raman and electronic spectra, the following data have been obtained. The equilibrium interatomic distance for N_2 in its ground state is 1.094 Å. The rotational energy may be calculated from the equation

$$E_{rot} \; (cm^{-1}) = [B + \alpha(V + \tfrac{1}{2})]J^2 + [D + \beta(V + \tfrac{1}{2})]J^4$$

where $J = 0, 1, 2, \ldots$ (the rotational quantum number), $V = 0, 1, 2, \ldots$ (the vibrational quantum number), $B = 2.003 \; cm^{-1}$, $\alpha = -0.023 \; cm^{-1}$, $D = -5.773 \times 10^{-6} \; cm^{-1}$, and $\beta = 8.61 \times 10^{-8} \; cm^{-1}$. The vibrational energy may be calculated from the equation

$$E_{vib} \; (cm^{-1}) = 2359.61(V + \tfrac{1}{2}) - 14.456(V + \tfrac{1}{2})^2$$

Gross Physical Properties

Solid: There are two crystalline forms of molecular nitrogen: a low-temperature, or α, form (cubic) and a higher-temperature, or β, form (hexagonal). The transition from α to β occurs at 35.62°K, with $\Delta H° = 54.7$ cal/mole. The density of the solid is 1.0265 g/cc at 20.6°K and 0.8792 at 63°K. The triple point is 63.18°K, at which point the vapor pressure is 94 mm. The heat of fusion is 172 cal/mole.

Liquid: The vapor pressure of liquid nitrogen may be calculated from the equation

$$\log P_{cm} = -\frac{339.8}{T} - 0.0056286\,T + 6.71057$$

The normal boiling point is 77.36°K (-195.79°C), at which temperature the heat of vaporization is 1335 cal/mole. The critical constants are 126.26°K, 33.54 atm, and 90.1 cc/mole. The surface tension and density may be calculated from the equations

$$\gamma \; (dynes/cm) = 11.68(1 - 0.00863\,T)$$
$$d \; (g/cc) = 1.1604 - 0.00455\,T$$

Gas: As one would expect from its electronic configuration, molecular nitrogen is diamagnetic. Its specific susceptibility is -0.430×10^{-6} at 20°. The viscosity, for pressures near one atmosphere, may be calculated from the equation η (cm^{-1} g sec^{-1}) $= KT^{3/2}/(C + T)$, where $K = 137.7 \times 10^{-7}$ and $C = 102.7$. The molar volume of nitrogen at 0°C and 1 atm is 22,402.5 cc/mole, as compared with the ideal-gas value of 22,414.0 cc/mole. At pressures between 0.5 and 1.0 atm and at temperatures between 77 and 90°K, $PV = nRT(1 - BP)$, with $B = 0.0022 + 19,600/T^3$ atm^{-1}.

The entropy of nitrogen gas at unit fugacity and 25°C is 45.767 cal/mole-deg, as calculated from molecular-constant data. This value is in good agreement with the third law value of 45.9 cal/mole-deg. The heat capacity at constant pressure at 25°C is 6.960 cal/mole-deg.

The volumes of nitrogen (STP) which dissolve in one volume of water when the partial pressure of nitrogen is one atmosphere are 0°, 0.0231; 20°, 0.0152; 30°, 0.0132; 50°, 0.0107; 100°, 0.0095.

2-4 ATOMIC NITROGEN

Active Nitrogen

When an electric discharge is established in nitrogen gas at a pressure of approximately 0.1 mm, a peach-colored glow is emitted. When the discharge is turned off, the gas continues to give off a yellow glow that lasts for several minutes. This glowing gas, called active nitrogen, consists mainly of ordinary molecular nitrogen and nitrogen atoms in their ground state. The existence of ground-state atoms in active nitrogen has been verified by at least three experiments:

1. The paramagnetic resonance spectrum of active nitrogen consists only of the triplet due to the ^4S state. (The observed coupling constant between the electronic and nuclear moment is 10.45 Mc/sec.)

2. In mass spectra of active nitrogen, the appearance potential of the mass-14 peak is about 14.8 eV, very close to the first ionization potential of atomic nitrogen (14.545 eV).

3. The 1200 Å absorption line of the ^4S-state atom has been observed in vacuum-ultraviolet spectra of active nitrogen.

The afterglow is caused by the emission-band spectra of excited states of the N_2 molecule that form by recombination of N atoms. The recombination is very slow because it can take place only by means of a three-body collision,

$$2N + M \rightarrow N_2 + M$$

where M (an N_2 molecule or the wall of the discharge tube) serves to carry off most of the recombination energy (225 kcal).

The concentration of atomic nitrogen in a stream of gas may be determined by *titrating* with nitric oxide:

$$N + NO \rightarrow N_2 + O$$

If nitric oxide is added at such a high rate that it is in excess, the unconsumed nitric oxide combines with the oxygen atoms formed, yielding a whitish- or greenish-yellow afterflow:

$$NO + O \rightarrow NO_2 + h\nu$$

If nitric oxide is added so slowly that atomic nitrogen is in excess, the nitrogen atoms react with the oxygen atoms, giving the typical blue color of the NO bands:

$$N + O + M \rightarrow NO^* + M$$

$$NO^* \rightarrow NO + h\nu$$

When the quantities of nitric oxide and atomic nitrogen are equal, the gas is practically colorless.

If active nitrogen is condensed on a surface cooled to 4°K and then allowed to warm up slowly, both heat and light are evolved. It has been suggested that, in the initial condensation, nitrogen atoms or radicals such as N_3 (or perhaps a mixture of these species) are quenched into a matrix of N_2 molecules. The infrared spectrum of the cold matrix and the emission spectrum of the warming matrix have been attributed to an N_3 radical. The paramagnetic resonance spectrum of the matrix is a triplet that has been ascribed to nitrogen atoms. However, the observed coupling constant of 12.08 Mc/sec is appreciably different from that of gaseous atomic nitrogen, and the reason for the discrepancy is not understood.

The ionization potentials of atomic nitrogen, in electron volts, are 14.545 (first), 29.605 (second), 47.426 (third), 77.450 (fourth), 97.863 (fifth), 551.92 (sixth), and 666.83 (seventh).

The Dissociation Energy of N_2

Several of the bands in the electronic spectrum of nitrogen are diffuse and cannot be extrapolated to a convergence limit. These diffuse bands are examples of predissociation, an effect that occurs when the vibrational levels of a certain electronic state overlap the dissociation continuum of another electronic state. In such cases a radiationless transition to the other dissociated state occurs. The breaking-off point, or predissociation limit, for the $C^3\pi_u$ state of N_2 occurs at 12.144 ± 0.005 eV above the ground state. This predissociation limit does not unambiguously yield the dissociation energy of nitrogen, because it is not immediately clear what the electronic states of the predissociated nitrogen atoms are.

The nitrogen atom has only three low-lying states that need be considered: the ^4S ground state and the ^2D and ^2P excited states, lying at 2.383 and 3.574 eV, respectively, above the ^4S state. In the ^4S state, all three $2p$ electrons have parallel spins. In the ^2D and ^2P states, two of the $2p$ electrons are paired; in the ^2D state, the *unpaired* electron has $m_l = 0$; in the ^2P state, the *paired* electrons have $m_l = 0$.

The dissociation energies for nitrogen corresponding to the various possible states for the dissociated atoms are given in Table 2-1. The $^4S + {}^4S$ possibility is eliminated because predissociation in the $a^1\pi$ and $b^3\pi$ states has been observed at energies less than 12 eV above the ground state. The $^2P + {}^2P$ and $^2D + {}^2P$ possibilities are eliminated because the $D_0(N_2)$ values corresponding to them are lower than the highest observed vibrational level of the ground state (6.33 eV). A large body of data indicates that, of the three remaining possibilities, the one with $D_0(N_2) = 9.762$ eV, or 225.1 kcal/mole, is correct. Two sets of data that lead to this choice of dissociation energy are given below.

Table 2-1   *Possible dissociation energies for N_2*

Possible predissociation products	$D_0(N_2)$, eV	Possible predissociation products	$D_0(N_2)$, eV
$^4S + {}^4S$	12.144	$^2D + {}^2D$	7.380
$^4S + {}^2D$	9.762	$^2D + {}^2P$	6.187
$^4S + {}^2P$	8.569	$^2P + {}^2P$	4.996

Electron-impact studies on molecular nitrogen show that N^+ ions appear at 24.27 eV. By subtracting the ionization potential of the nitrogen atom (14.54 eV) from this value, we calculate $D(N_2) = 9.73$ eV, in good agreement with the 9.762-eV spectroscopic value. However, by assuming that the electron impact produces an excited N atom (^2D, 2.38 eV) or an excited N^+ ion (^1D, 1.90 eV), the value of $D(N_2)$ may be brought down to 7.35 or 7.83 eV. Thus the electron-impact data are in fair agreement with either the 9.762 or the 7.380 spectroscopic value, but not with the 8.569 value.

An equimolar mixture of cyanogen and oxygen burns as follows:

$$(CN)_2 + O_2 \rightarrow 2CO + N_2$$

If one calculates the equilibrium temperature and composition for this flame using $D(N_2) = 9.762$ eV, one calculates a temperature of 4850°K and predicts practically no dissociation to N atoms. On the other hand, if one uses $D(N_2) = 7.380$ eV, one calculates a temperature of 4350°K and a considerable dissociation to N atoms. By determining the relative intensities of vibrational transitions in the CN bands of such a flame, a temperature of 4800 ± 200°K was measured. This measurement obviously supports the 9.762-eV value.

2-5 THE NITROGEN NUCLEUS

Nitrogen Isotopes

Ordinary nitrogen, with an atomic weight of 14.0067, consists of N^{14} (with an atomic weight of 14.00308) and N^{15} (with an atomic weight of 15.00011) in the percentage abundances 99.635 and 0.365, respectively. The nitrogen-14 nucleus has a spin moment of 1, a magnetic dipole moment of $+0.40357$ nuclear magnetons, and an electric quadrupole moment of $+0.02$ *barn* (10^{-24} cm²). The nitrogen-15 nucleus has a spin moment of $\frac{1}{2}$, a magnetic dipole moment of -0.28304 nuclear magnetons, and no electric quadrupole moment.

Nitrogen 15 may be separated from nitrogen 14 by thermal diffusion, chemical exchange, or a combination of the two. The following exchange reactions have been used for preparing concentrated N^{15}:

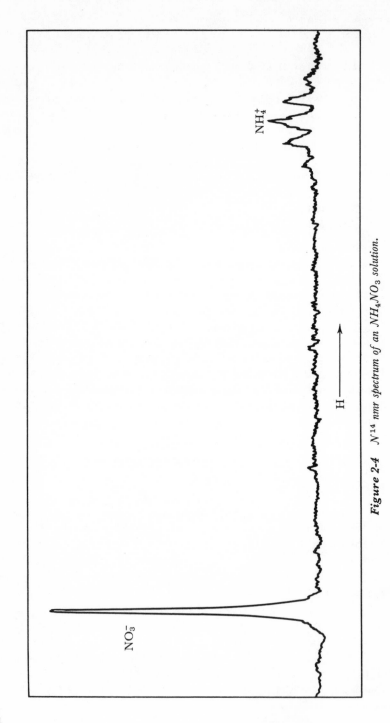

Figure 2-4 N^{14} *nmr spectrum of an* NH_4NO_3 *solution.*

$$N^{15}H_3(g) + N^{14}H_4^+(aq) = N^{14}H_3(g) + N^{15}H_4^+(aq)$$

$$N^{15}O(g) + N^{14}O_3^-(aq) = N^{14}O(g) + N^{15}O_3^-(aq)$$

$$N^{14}O_2(g) + N^{15}O(g) = N^{15}O_2(g) + N^{14}O(g)$$

The first and second reactions involve two separate phases and have been used in countercurrent cascade processes. The NO-NO_3^- exchange reaction has given a steady-state product containing 99.8 per cent N^{15}. The third, gas-phase NO-NO_2 equilibrium has been found to contribute to the separation in a thermal diffusion column containing a mixture of these gases. Very efficient concentration of N^{15} has been effected by the simple fractional distillation of NO.

All the known radioactive isotopes of nitrogen have such short half-lives that they are of no use for tagging nitrogen atoms in chemical reactions. Nitrogen 12 is a positron and alpha emitter with a half-life of 0.0125 sec, β^+ energy of 16.6 MeV, and α energy (total for three alpha particles) of about 4 MeV. Nitrogen 13 is a positron emitter with a half-life of 10.05 min and β^+ energy of 1.2 MeV. Nitrogen 16 is a beta-electron and gamma-ray emitter with a half-life of 7.35 sec, β^- energies of 10.40 MeV (28 per cent), 4.39 MeV (54 per cent), and 3.32 MeV (18 per cent), and a set of γ energies. Nitrogen 17 is a beta-electron and neutron-emitter with a half-life of 4.14 sec, a β^- energy of 3.7 MeV, and a mean neutron energy of 0.9 MeV.

Nuclear Magnetic Resonance

The nuclear magnetic resonance frequency for an isolated N^{14} nucleus is 3.076 Mc for a 10,000 gauss magnetic field. In actual practice, the frequency of the resonance depends strongly on the chemical compound chosen. Thus, for a solution of ammonium nitrate, two resonances appear: they are separated by about 1 kc/sec. One resonance corresponds to the NH_4^+ ion; the other corresponds to the NO_3^- ion.

The nmr spectrum of a slightly acidic solution of ammonium nitrate is given in Figure 2-4. It will be noted that the high-field resonance (due to NH_4^+) is split into a quintet because of the coupling of the magnetic moment of the nitrogen nucleus with the moments of the four equivalent protons (each with spin $\frac{1}{2}$). The chemical shifts of N^{14} in various species relative to NO_3^- ion are given in Table 2-2. It will be noted that species in which the

Table 2-2 N^{14} *chemical shifts*

Species	δ, ppm	Species	δ, ppm
NH_4^+	348	SCN^-	152
N_2H_4	312	CN^-	126
$N(CH_3)_4^+$	298	N_2	14
NH_3	290	NO_3^-	0
NH_3OH^+	266	NO_2^-	-254

electronic structure of the nitrogen is more spherically symmetric resonate at higher fields. Thus the symmetric NH_4^+ ion has the highest chemical shift in the table, whereas the NO_2^- ion, with a very asymmetric electric field around the nitrogen atom, has the lowest chemical shift.

Since N^{14} has a quadrupole moment, a species with a nitrogen atom in an asymmetric electron distribution has a broad nmr signal. This quadrupole broadening is so great in some compounds as to make the signal essentially unobservable, and any fine structure is wiped out. This difficulty may be eliminated by using the N^{15} isotope, which has no quadrupole moment and which resonates at 4.315 Mc in a 10,000 gauss field.

Symmetric and Antisymmetric Rotational Levels

Since N^{14} has a nuclear spin of 1, there are three possible values for the resultant nuclear spin of the N_2 molecule, namely, 0, 1, and 2, with statistical weights 1, 3, and 5, respectively. Now, the symmetric rotational levels of the molecule have even values of resultant nuclear spin and the antisymmetric levels have odd values of resultant nuclear spin. Because the ratio of the number of symmetric levels to the number of antisymmetric levels is $(1 + 5)$ to 3, there is an intensity alternation in the ratio 2:1 in the lines of the pure rotational Raman spectrum of nitrogen. As a matter of fact, this intensity alternation is one of the best proofs that the nuclear spin of N^{14} is 1.

Nuclear Quadrupole Resonance

The coupling of the nuclear quadrupole moment of N^{14} to the neighboring electrons provides potentially very useful information about the bonds in nitrogen-containing molecules. The

Table 2-3 N^{14} *quadrupole coupling constants*

Compound	eqQ
NH_3	-4.1
NF_3	-7.07
ClCN	-3.63
HCN	-4.7
CH_3NC	$+0.5$
N_2O (outer nitrogen)	-1.03
N_2O (inner nitrogen)	-0.27

electrostatic interaction between the nucleus and the electrostatic field at the nucleus exerts a torque on the molecule that modifies its rotational levels and gives rise to hyperfine structure in the rotational spectrum.

The quadrupole coupling constant eqQ may be experimentally determined either from pure quadrupole spectra or from the hyperfine structure in microwave rotational spectra. Clearly, if the electron cloud of a nitrogen atom is spherically symmetric, the quantity eqQ should be zero. On the other hand, if the electron cloud is very asymmetric, a large value of eqQ should be observed. Quadrupole coupling constants for several compounds are given in Table 2-3. It will be noted that in compounds where nitrogen is tetracovalent, and consequently in a somewhat symmetric cloud of electrons, eqQ is small. This is the case in $CH_3-\overset{+}{N}\equiv\overset{-}{C}$ and for the inner nitrogen atom of $\overset{-}{N}=\overset{+}{N}=O$. As one might expect, the outer nitrogen atom of N_2O has a larger coupling constant.

REFERENCES

D. M. Yost and H. Russell, Jr., *Systematic Inorganic Chemistry*, Prentice-Hall, Englewood Cliffs, N.J., 1946.

G. Herzberg, *Spectra of Diatomic Molecules*, 2d ed., Van Nostrand, Princeton, N.J., 1950.

K. R. Jennings and J. W. Linnett, "Active nitrogen," *Quart. Rev. (London)*, **12**, 116 (1958).

A. M. Bass and H. P. Broida (eds.), *Formation and Trapping of Free Radicals*, Academic, New York, 1960.

C. H. Townes and A. L. Schawlow, *Microwave Spectroscopy*, McGraw-Hill, New York, 1955.

"Selected values of chemical thermodynamic constants," *Natl. Bur. Standards Circ. 500*, 1952.

D. Strominger, J. M. Hollander, and G. T. Seaborg, "Table of isotopes," *Rev. Mod. Phys.*, **30**, 585 (1958).

B. P. Dailey, "Nuclear quadrupole resonance," *J. Phys. Chem.*, **57**, 490 (1953).

A. G. Gaydon, *Dissociation Energies and Spectra of Diatomic Molecules*, 2d ed., Chapman & Hall, London, 1953.

3

Ammonia

3-1 PREPARATION

Most ammonia is manufactured by the Haber process.   In this process, hydrogen and nitrogen react at high temperatures and pressures and in the presence of an iron catalyst according to the reversible reaction

$$N_2(g) + 3H_2(g) = 2NH_3(g)$$

The effect of temperature and pressure on the equilibrium is given in Table 3-1.   The formation of ammonia is obviously favored by both low temperatures and high pressures, but if the temperature falls much below 400°, the rate of the catalyzed reaction is too slow for economical production.   On the other hand, if the temperature is too high, the equilibrium pressure of ammonia is too low for satisfactory yields.   In practice, pressures of about 1000 atm and temperatures of about 500° are employed.

The small amount of water in commercial ammonia prepared by the Haber process may be completely removed by condensing the ammonia as a liquid on metallic sodium.   The sodium dissolves

Table 3-1   *Volume percentage of ammonia in* $3:1$ H_2—N_2 *equilibrium mixtures*

Temp, °C	Pressure, atm				
	10	30	100	300	1000
300	14.73	30.25	52.04	70.96	92.55
400	3.85	10.15	25.12	47.00	79.82
500	1.21	3.49	10.61	26.44	57.47
600	0.49	1.39	4.52	13.77	31.43

(to form a blue solution) and reacts with any trace of water in the solution. A simple distillation then yields extremely pure ammonia.

Deuterio-ammonia is readily prepared by the action of deuterium oxide vapor on magnesium nitride:

$$3D_2O + Mg_3N_2 \rightarrow 2ND_3 + 3MgO$$

3-2 STRUCTURE

The ammonia molecule has the form of a pyramid with the nitrogen atom at the apex and the hydrogen atoms at the corners of the base, which is an equilateral triangle. Various molecular constants for ammonia are given in Table 3-2.

It is instructive to look upon the ammonia molecule as the result of transferring one of the protons in CH_4 to the carbon nucleus. In this process, the four C—H bonds are converted to three N—H bonds and a lone pair of electrons. If this process were to take place without any subsequent rearrangement of the electrons and protons, we would find the three protons and the lone pair at the corners of a regular tetrahedron. That is, the orbitals of the nitrogen atom would be hybridized as sp^3. However, the electrostatic repulsion between the lone pair of electrons and any pair of the bonding electrons is much greater than the repulsion between any two pairs of bonding electrons. Therefore, the three N—H bonds are pushed into a more stable configuration wherein the H—N—H bond angle has decreased from the tetrahedral angle of 109° 28′ to the observed angle of 106° 47′.

The bonding in ammonia may be discussed in a different manner. Let us consider the process of bringing three hydrogen

Table 3-2 *Molecular constants of ammonia*

Constant	NH_3		ND_3
Moments of inertia			
I_B (10^{-40} g cm²)	2.816		5.448
I_A (10^{-40} g cm²)	4.44		8.87
r_0 (N—H) (Å)		1.014	
Height of pyramid, Å		0.381	
H—N—H angle		106° 47′	
Fundamental vibration *frequencies*			
ν_1	3335.9 cm^{-1}		2419 cm^{-1}
	3337.5		
ν_2	931.58		748.6
	968.08		749.0
ν_3	3414		2555
ν_4	1627.5		1191.0
Dipole moment (10^{-18} esu)	1.47		1.50

atoms up to a nitrogen atom in its ground state. The bonding would logically take place through the three unpaired p electrons along three mutually perpendicular axes. In the absence of any other effects, one would expect the ammonia molecule to be pyramidal with an H—N—H angle of 90°. However, the mutual repulsion of the partially positively charged hydrogen atoms and the repulsion of the pairs of bonding electrons cause the bond angle to increase up to 106° 47′.

The two preceding explanations of the bonding in NH_3 are quite different in their approaches and serve to emphasize the fact that the bond angles of a molecule are the result of a very fine balance between electrostatic repulsive forces and hybridization energies.

The nitrogen atom of the ammonia molecule has two equivalent positions of equilibrium on either side of the plane of the three hydrogen atoms. The potential function for the nitrogen atom is thus represented by two wells that are separated by a potential hill (see Figure 3-1). It can be shown that, for such a potential, the

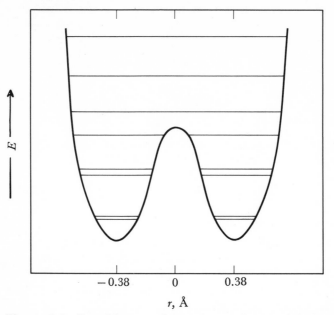

Figure 3-1 *Potential energy of ammonia as a function of the distance of the nitrogen atom from the plane of the hydrogen atoms.*

energy levels below the top of the potential hill are doubled.   For ammonia, the inversion doublet separation amounts to 23,786 Mc in the ground state.

The doubling of the energy levels is very obvious in the vibration-rotation bands of ammonia, which consist of a series of doublets.   Direct transitions within a given doublet may be observed in microwave spectra, and such transitions have been used in the ammonia beam maser.[1]   The ammonia beam maser, pictured schematically in Figure 3-2, consists of a beam of ammonia molecules which passes through an electrostatic focuser into a microwave resonance cavity.   The molecules in the beam are mainly in the lowest vibrational energy level, with approximately equal numbers of molecules in the two inversion levels.

In the radially inhomogeneous field of the electrostatic focuser,

[1] The word *maser* is an acronym for *microwave amplification* by *stimulated emission* of *radiation*.

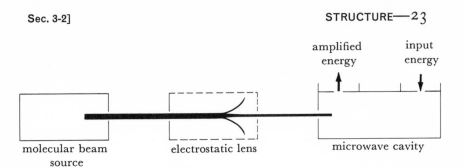

Figure 3-2 *Schematic diagram of ammonia beam maser.*

the lower-state molecules experience an outward radial force and the upper-state molecules experience an inward radial force. Thus only the upper-state molecules are focused to enter the microwave cavity. The microwave cavity is tuned to the inversion doublet frequency,[2] and an entering microwave signal of this frequency induces the molecules to radiate in phase at the same frequency. A coherently amplified signal of very high spectral purity issues from the output waveguide. The apparatus has been used as a frequency standard and has been found to be reproducible to better than one part in 10^{10}.

In solid ammonia, each nitrogen atom is situated on a three-fold axis of symmetry and is surrounded at a distance of 3.38 Å by six nearest-neighbor nitrogen atoms in two groups of three. The three neighboring atoms on one side form angles of 71.66°; the three on the other side form angles of 118.05°. The six neighboring nitrogen atoms are bound by asymmetric hydrogen bonds, but the hydrogen atoms do not lie exactly on the lines between the nitrogen atoms. The three closest hydrogen atoms are those in the bonds to the nitrogen atoms at 118.05° angles. These hydrogen atoms are at a distance of 1.13 Å and form H—N—H angles of 107°. The bond angle is very close to that for gaseous NH_3, but the bond distance is considerably longer than that for gaseous NH_3 (1.014 Å). A longer bond distance is to be expected in the hydrogen-bonded solid.

[2] Transitions among the various rotational levels of ammonia cause fine structure in the NH_3 inversion spectrum. Ammonia molecular beam masers generally use the 3,3 line at 23,870.11 Mc because it is very intense.

3-3 PHYSICAL PROPERTIES

Various physical and thermodynamic properties of ammonia are summarized in Table 3-3.

Table 3-3 *Some physical properties of ammonia*

Triple point	195.46°K
Triple-point pressure	45.58 mm
Vapor pressure of solid	$\log_{10} P_{mm} = 9.98379 - 1627.22/T$
Heat of fusion	1351.6 cal/mole
Boiling point	239.78°K
Vapor pressure of liquid (for $T < 250°K$)	$\log_{10} P_{mm} = 9.95028 - 1473.17/T - 0.0038603\ T$
Heat of vaporization at bp	5581 cal/mole
Critical pressure	112.3 atm
Critical temperature	405.6°K
Entropy	
0 to 15°K, Debye fn. $hcv/k = 210$	0.056
15°K to melting point	10.16
Fusion	6.919
Melting point to boiling point	3.646
Vaporization	23.29
Entropy of actual gas at bp	44.06 $\pm$ 0.10 eu
Thermodynamic functions for gas	
ΔH_f° at 25°C	− 11.04 kcal/mole
ΔF_f° at 25°C	− 3.976 kcal/mole
S° at 25°C	46.01 eu
C_p° at 25°C	8.523 cal/mole-deg

Density of liquid

t, °C	density, g/cc	t, °C	density, g/cc
− 70	0.7253	− 20	0.6650
− 60	.7138	− 10	.6520
− 50	.7020	0	.6386
− 40	.6900	10	.6247
− 34	.6826	20	.6103
− 33	.6814	25	.6028
− 30	0.6776	30	0.5952

Viscosity of liquid

t, °C	viscosity, centipoises	t, °C	viscosity, centipoises
− 33.5	0.254	10	0.152
− 26	.230	15	.146
− 10	.183	20	.141
− 4	.170	25	.135
5	0.162	30	0.138

(cont.)

Table 3-3   *Some physical properties of ammonia (continued)*

Dielectric constant of liquid

t, °C	Dielec. const	t, °C	Dielec. const
−33	~23	25	16.90
5	18.94	35	16.26
15	17.82		

Surface tension of liquid

t, °C	γ, erg/cm²
11.10	23.38
34.05	18.05
58.98	12.95

where $t = $ °C, $\gamma = 23.41 - 0.3371t - 0.000943t^2$ ($-75 < t < -39$)

Electrical conductivity of liquid $L_0 \sim 1 \times 10^{-11}$ ohm^{-1} cm^{-1} (very pure NH_3)

Refractive index of liquid   1.325 at 16°C for $\lambda = 5899$ Å

Crystal data   Cubic, 4 molecules per unit cell at $-185°$

$$a_0 = 5.2253 \ kX$$
$$= 5.2358 \text{ Å}$$

Calculated density = 0.7881 g/cc

3-4   LIQUID-AMMONIA SOLUTIONS

Dielectric Constant

Liquid ammonia, in spite of its low boiling point ($-33.38°$) and pungent odor, is one of the most extensively studied non-aqueous solvents. It certainly is the most important inorganic solvent besides water. Many of the properties that make ammonia a good solvent are consequences of the high dipole moment of the ammonia molecule. For example, the high dielectric constant (ca. 23 at the boiling point) is a consequence of the polarity of the molecule. The solvation energy of a gaseous ion of radius r and charge e is given by the Born equation

$$\Delta E = \frac{e^2}{2r} \left(1 - \frac{1}{\epsilon} \right)$$

Many salts dissolve in liquid ammonia to form highly conducting solutions. The solubilities of some inorganic salts in liquid ammonia at 25° are listed in Table 3-4. It should be pointed out that most of these salts form ammoniates, and the solid phases in equilibrium with the saturated solutions are not necessarily those shown.

Table 3-4   *Solubilities of salts in liquid ammonia at 25°*
(grams per 100 g of NH_3)

Salt	Solubility	Salt	Solubility
NH_4Cl	102.5	KCl	0.04
NH_4Br	237.9	KBr	13.50
NH_4I	368.5	KI	182.0
NH_4SCN	312.0	KCNO	1.70
NH_4ClO_4	137.9	$KClO_3$	2.52
NH_4NO_3	390.0	$KBrO_3$	0.002
$NH_4C_2H_3O_2$	253.2	KNO_3	10.4
$(NH_4)_2SO_3$	0.0	KNH_2	3.6
$(NH_4)_2HPO_4$	0.0	KIO_3	0.0
NH_4HCO_3	0.0	K_2SO_4	0.0
$(NH_4)_2CO_3$	0.0	K_2CO_3	0.0
$LiNO_3$	243.7	AgCl	0.83
Li_2SO_4	0.0	AgBr	5.92
		AgI	206.8
NaF	0.35	$AgNO_3$	86.04
NaCl	3.02		
NaBr	138.0	$Ca(NO_3)_2$	80.22
NaI	161.9	$Sr(NO_3)_2$	87.08
NaSCN	205.5	$Ba(NO_3)_2$	97.22
$NaNO_3$	97.6	$BaCl_2$	0.0
$Na_2S_2O_3$	0.17		
$NaNH_2$	0.17	MnI_2	0.02
Na_2SO_4	0.0	ZnI_2	0.10
		H_3BO_3	1.92
		TlCl	0.62

Because it has a much smaller dielectric constant than water ($\epsilon = 82$ for water at 25°), ammonia shows a much higher solubility for organic compounds than does water. Thus, although the alkanes are only slightly soluble in ammonia, they are more soluble in ammonia than in water. Benzene is very soluble. Diethyl ether is moderately soluble, but higher molecular weight ethers are less so.

Hydrogen Bonding

Ammonia, like water, hydrogen fluoride, alcohols, carboxylic acids, etc., forms strong hydrogen bonds. The effect of hydrogen

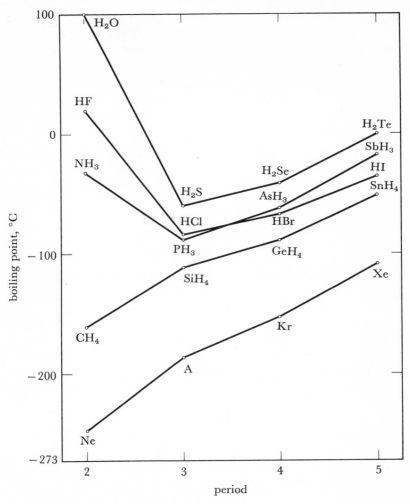

Figure 3-3　*Boiling points of hydrides.*

bonding on the boiling points of ammonia, water, and hydrogen fluoride can be seen in Fig. 3-3, from which it is obvious that the heavier hydrides such as HCl, H_2S, and PH_3 are "normal" un-associated liquids. The heat and entropy of vaporization of ammonia are abnormally high because in the process of vaporization not only must the weak Van der Waals forces between molecules be broken but a definite amount of hydrogen-bonded structure must also be broken down.   The influence of hydrogen bonding on solubilities can be seen in the fact that phenol, aniline, and simple alcohols and amines are miscible with ammonia in all proportions.

Acid-Base Properties

The acid-base character of ammonia greatly influences solubilities and chemical reactions in liquid ammonia.   An ammonia molecule can either lose a proton to form the basic amide ion or gain a proton to form the acidic ammonium ion.   Both processes take place in the self-ionization reaction

$$2NH_3 = NH_4^+ + NH_2^- \qquad K_{-33°} \sim 10^{-30}$$

From the magnitude of the constant, it is clear that one can operate over an extremely wide range of ammonium ion concentrations in liquid ammonia—all the way from $[NH_4^+] = 1$ as in $1\,M$ NH_4Cl to $[NH_4^+] = 10^{-30}$ as in $1\,M$ KNH_2.   Relatively strong protonic acids such as the hydrogen halides and carboxylic acids react with ammonia to form ammonium salts.   The ammonium salts of most monobasic acids (except HF and high-molecular-weight carboxylic acids) are soluble.

$$HCl + NH_3 \rightarrow NH_4^+ + Cl^-$$

$$CH_3COOH + NH_3 \rightarrow NH_4^+ + CH_3COO^-$$

Since such acids are strong in ammonia and hence all of the same strength, it is often said that ammonia is an "acid leveling" solvent.   Thus, the acidities of weak acids are accentuated in ammonia and it is possible to form salts of such weak acids as water, arsine, and triphenylmethane:

$$K^+ + NH_2^- + H_2O \rightarrow NH_3 + KOH$$

$$NH_2^- + AsH_3 \rightarrow NH_3 + AsH_2^-$$

$$NH_2^- + (C_6H_5)_3CH \rightarrow NH_3 + (C_6H_5)_3C^-$$

Many compounds, such as oxides and halides of the less electropositive elements, undergo ammonolysis in liquid ammonia to form ammonium ions and either amido, imido, or nitrido complexes:

$$CO_2 + 2NH_3 \rightarrow NH_4(CO_2NH_2)$$

$$HgCl_2 + 2NH_3 \rightarrow HgNH_2Cl + NH_4^+ + Cl^-$$

$$PCl_3 + 6NH_3 \rightarrow P(NH_2)_3 + 3NH_4^+ + 3Cl^-$$

$$GeI_4 + 6NH_3 \rightarrow Ge(NH)_2 + 4NH_4^+ + 4I^-$$

$$3SiH_3Cl + 4NH_3 \rightarrow N(SiH_3)_3 + 3NH_4^+ + 3Cl^-$$

A few compounds, such as saline hydrides and basic oxides, are more basic than the amide ion.   Such compounds can remove protons from ammonia molecules.

$$LiH + NH_3 \rightarrow LiNH_2 + H_2$$

$$Na_2O + NH_3 \rightarrow NaNH_2 + NaOH$$

Ammonia System of Compounds

Just as many familiar oxygen compounds can be thought of as being derived from the solvent water, so can many nitrogen compounds be looked upon as derivatives of ammonia.   Thus we can establish a set of *ammono compounds* each of which has an analogous aquo compound (see Table 3-5).   Since structurally analogous compounds often react in analogous ways, such considerations have been very useful in synthetic chemistry.

It has even been suggested that on planets with ammonia atmospheres (e.g., Jupiter) there exist forms of life which use ammono-proteins, ammono-carbohydrates, etc. (see Figure 3-4).

Table 3-5   *Some ammono and aquo compounds*

Ammono compound	Aquo compound	Ammono compound	Aquo compound
NH_3	H_2O	Li_2NH	Li_2O
KNH_2	KOH	NH_2NO_2	HNO_3
NH_4Cl	HCl	$HN{=}C(NH_2)_2$	$O{=}C(OH)_2$
CH_3CONH_2	CH_3COOH	$SO_2(NH_2)_2$	$SO_2(OH)_2$

"AMMONIA! AMMONIA!"

Figure 3-4

3-5 METAL-AMMONIA SOLUTIONS

Liquid ammonia possesses the remarkable property of being able to dissolve electropositive metals reversibly. The dilute solutions, which have a beautiful blue color, have been the subject of many investigations. The factors that cause a metal to have a high oxidation potential (high ionic solvation energy, low ionization potential, low sublimation energy) are the same as those that cause it to have a high solubility in ammonia. Thus the alkali metals, the alkaline-earth metals (except beryllium), europium, and ytterbium are soluble. The solubilities of some metals are given in Table 3-6.

At low concentrations of the alkali metals, the molar paramagnetic susceptibility of the solutions corresponds to one unpaired electron per metal atom. At higher concentrations (above $0.1\ M$) the molar susceptibility is very low and corresponds to essentially complete pairing of electrons.

The electrical conductivity of alkali-metal solutions is very high—higher than found for any other electrolyte in any known

Table 3-6   *Solubilities of alkali metals in ammonia*

Metal	Temp	G-atom metal per 1000 g NH_3	Moles NH_3 per g-atom metal
Lithium	0	16.31	3.60
	−33.2	15.66	3.75
	−63.5	15.41	3.81
Sodium	22	9.56	6.14
	0	10.00	5.87
	−33.8	10.72	5.48
	−50	10.89	5.39
	−70	11.29	5.20
Potassium	0	12.4	4.7
	−33.2	11.86	4.95
	−50	12.3	4.9
Cesium	−50	25.1	2.34

solvent.   As a dilute metal solution becomes more concentrated, the molar conductivity falls because of a decrease in the concentration of electrical carriers per mole of dissolved metal.   But upon continued concentration of the solution, the conductivity rises sharply, and for the saturated solution the conductivity approaches that for pure metals (see Fig. 3-5).

The absorption spectra of all the metal solutions are practically identical.   The spectrum consists of a very intense, broad band with a maximum at 15,000 Å.

The physical properties of metal-ammonia solutions have been explained by assuming that metals dissolve to form ammoniated metal ions and ammoniated electrons.   In dilute solutions ($< 0.001 \, M$) these species are essentially independent.   Each ammoniated electron is believed to exist in a large cavity in the solvent and to be stabilized by the orientation of ammonia dipoles on the periphery of the cavity.   In solutions of moderate concentration ($\sim 0.01 \, M$) ionic aggregation reactions of the following types take place.

$$M^+ + e_{am}^- = M$$

$$2M^+ + 2e_{am}^- = M_2$$

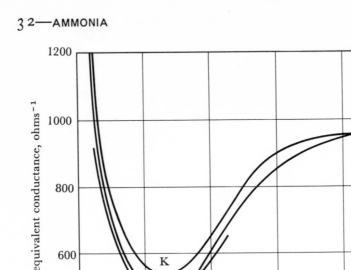

Figure 3-5   *The equivalent conductance of solutions of potassium, sodium, and lithium in liquid ammonia at* $-33.5°C$. $V =$ *liters of ammonia per gram-atom of metal.*

The monomer M may be considered a simple ion pair in which the ammoniated metal ion and ammoniated electron are held together by coulombic forces.   Similarly, the dimer M_2 may be considered a quadrupolar ionic assembly of two ammoniated metal ions and two ammoniated electrons in which the electrons have opposed spins.

In more concentrated solutions, still further ionic aggregation occurs.   However, in highly concentrated solutions, there are insufficient ammonia molecules to coordinate the electrons, and the latter are then free to participate in metallic bonding and conduction.

Reactions of Metal-Ammonia Solutions

All metal-ammonia solutions are metastable with respect to decomposition to hydrogen and the metal amide:

$$M + xNH_3 \rightarrow \frac{x}{2} H_2 + M(NH_2)_x$$

This reaction is very slow if the solutions are kept cold and clean, but it can be made to proceed very rapidly if suitable catalysts such as transition-metal salts are added.

Most of the reactions involving metal-ammonia solutions may be considered as proceeding through one of the following three initial steps: (1) simple electron addition without bond cleavage,

$$e_{am}^- + X \rightarrow X^-$$

(2) bond cleavage by the addition of one electron,

$$e_{am}^- + X—Y \rightarrow X\cdot + Y^-$$

or (3) bond cleavage by the addition of two electrons,

$$2e_{am}^- + X—Y \rightarrow X^- + Y^-$$

1. The following reactions are examples of simple electron addition without bond cleavage.

$$e_{am}^- + O_2 \rightarrow O_2^-$$
$$e_{am}^- + (CH_3)_3Sn\cdot \rightarrow (CH_3)_3Sn:^-$$
$$e_{am}^- + MnO_4^- \rightarrow MnO_4^{2-}$$
$$2e_{am}^- + Ni(CN)_4^{2-} \rightarrow Ni(CN)_4^{4-}$$

2. The following reactions involve a bond cleavage and the addition of one electron.

$$e_{am}^- + NH_4^+ \rightarrow NH_3 + \tfrac{1}{2}H_2$$
$$e_{am}^- + AsH_3 \rightarrow AsH_2^- + \tfrac{1}{2}H_2$$
$$e_{am}^- + RC{\equiv}CH \rightarrow RC{\equiv}C:^- + \tfrac{1}{2}H_2$$
$$e_{am}^- + R_2S \rightarrow RS^- + \tfrac{1}{2}R—R$$
$$e_{am}^- + (C_2H_5)_3SnBr \rightarrow (C_2H_5)_3Sn\cdot + Br^-$$

The radical that first forms usually undergoes dimerization, as in the first four reactions above. Occasionally, as in the last reaction, the radical is stable in ammonia.

3. When the addition of two electrons causes bond cleavage, either two anions form or a *dianion* forms:

$$2e_{am}^- + Ge_2H_6 \rightarrow 2GeH_3^-$$
$$2e_{am}^- + C_6H_5NHNH_2 \rightarrow C_6H_5NH^- + NH_2^-$$
$$2e_{am}^- + C_6H_5—N{=}O \rightarrow C_6H_5—N{=}\!{=}O^-$$

Usually one or both of the anions undergoes ammonolysis, as in the following examples:

$$2e_{am}^- + N_2O + NH_3 \rightarrow N_2 + OH^- + NH_2^-$$

$$2e_{am}^- + NCO^- + NH_3 \rightarrow CN^- + OH^- + NH_2^-$$

$$2e_{am}^- + C_2H_5Br + NH_3 \rightarrow Br^- + C_2H_6 + NH_2^-$$

$$2e_{am}^- + RCH{=}CH_2 + 2NH_3 \rightarrow RCH_2CH_3 + 2NH_2^-$$

3-6   AMIDES, IMIDES, AND NITRIDES

Amides

We have already pointed out that the alkali and alkaline-earth amides may be prepared by reaction of the metals with liquid ammonia in the presence of suitable catalysts:

$$M + xNH_3 \rightarrow M(NH_2)_x + \frac{x}{2}H_2$$

The same reaction may be carried out at elevated temperatures with gaseous ammonia.   In another method, a dispersion of alkali metal in mineral oil is treated with ammonia at room temperature. The direct synthesis of sodium amide from the elements

$$Na + \tfrac{1}{2}N_2 + H_2 \rightarrow NaNH_2$$

takes place at 350 to 450° at pressures of 30 to 50 atm.   Alkali amides may be prepared by the electrolysis of salt solutions in liquid ammonia:

$$NH_3 + e^- = NH_2^- + \tfrac{1}{2}H_2$$

Amides of lithium, the alkaline earths, silver, zinc, cadmium, manganese, and nickel may be precipitated by adding potassium amide to liquid-ammonia solutions of soluble salts of these metals. These same amides, as well as those of sodium and potassium, may be prepared by treating the corresponding metal alkyls or metal aryls with ammonia:

$$NaC_6H_5 + NH_3 \rightarrow NaNH_2 + C_6H_6$$

$$Zn(C_2H_5)_2 + 2NH_3 \rightarrow Zn(NH_2)_2 + 2C_2H_6$$

Silver amide is explosive.

Proton magnetic resonance and infrared spectra yield an N—H distance of 1.03 Å and a bond angle of approximately 104°

Table 3-7   *Some properties of the alkali amides*

Compound	Melting point, °C	Density, 25°	ΔH_f°, kcal/mole, 25°	Solubility in liquid ammonia, 25°
$LiNH_2$	373–375	1.18	−43.5	~0
$NaNH_2$	208	1.39	−28.4	0.17 g/100 g
KNH_2	338	1.64	−28.3	3.6 g/100 g
$RbNH_2$	309	2.58	−25.7	Very soluble
$CsNH_2$	262	3.43	−25.4	Very soluble
$Ca(NH_2)_2$			−91.6	~0
$Sr(NH_2)_2$			−83.2	~0
$Ba(NH_2)_2$			−78.9	~0
$Zn(NH_2)_2$		2.13	−38.8	~0
$Cd(NH_2)_2$		3.05	−14.7	~0

for the amide ion.   Some properties of amides are presented in Table 3-7.   Each of the amides listed in Table 3-7 reacts vigorously with water to form the corresponding hydroxide and ammonia:

$$M(NH_2)_x + xH_2O \rightarrow M(OH)_x + xNH_3$$

Sodium cyanide is made on a large scale by the reduction of sodium amide with carbon at red heat:

$$NaNH_2 + C \rightarrow NaCN + H_2$$

Sodium amide finds considerable use in organic syntheses as a reagent for the introduction of amino groups into molecules,

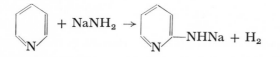

for dehydration,

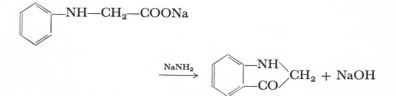

for sodium salt formation,

$$RC{\equiv}CH + NaNH_2 \rightarrow RC{\equiv}CNa + NH_3$$

and for dehydrohalogenation,

$$\underset{\displaystyle CH_3-\overset{\displaystyle C_6H_5}{\overset{|}{C}H}-CH_2Br}{} + NaNH_2 \rightarrow$$

$$\underset{\displaystyle CH_3-\overset{\displaystyle C_6H_5}{\overset{|}{C}}{=}CH_2}{} + NaBr + NH_3$$

Imides and Nitrides

In general, when a metal amide is heated, deammoniation to the corresponding metal nitride occurs.

$$3Mg(NH_2)_2 \rightarrow Mg_3N_2 + 4NH_3$$

$$3Cd(NH_2)_2 \rightarrow Cd_3N_2 + 4NH_3$$

Lithium amide is unusual in that it decomposes first to the imide:

$$2LiNH_2 \rightarrow Li_2NH + NH_3$$

In order to prepare a pure product, it is necessary to avoid melting the amide and decomposing the imide. This is accomplished by heating the amide to 360° under vacuum until almost complete evolution of ammonia, followed by raising the temperature to 450°. At higher temperatures, lithium imide decomposes to the nitride, Li_3N (mp 849°). Sodium nitride cannot be prepared in this manner. At temperatures above 335°, sodium amide decomposes to the elements

$$NaNH_2 \rightarrow Na + \tfrac{1}{2}N_2 + H_2$$

if the gaseous products are pumped away and the partial pressure of hydrogen is kept below the decomposition pressure of sodium hydride. If the partial pressure of hydrogen is kept above the decomposition pressure of sodium hydride, decomposition to sodium hydride takes place:

$$NaNH_2 \rightarrow NaH + \tfrac{1}{2}N_2 + \tfrac{1}{2}H_2$$

Some metal nitrides may be precipitated by adding potassium amide to liquid-ammonia solutions of the appropriate metal salts. Thus one may prepare Cu_3N, Hg_3N_2, AlN, Tl_3N, and BiN.

The most widely applicable method for preparing nitrides is that in which the metal (or a mixture of the metal oxide and carbon) is heated with nitrogen or ammonia. This method is applicable to the following nitrides, all of which are thermodynamically stable with respect to the elements: Li_3N, Be_3N_2, Mg_3N_2, Ca_3N_2, Sr_3N_2, Ba_3N_2, *BN*, *AlN*, *ScN*, *YN*, *LaN*, *CeN*, *GaN*, *InN*, Si_3N_4, **TiN**, **ZrN**, **HfN**, Th_3N_4, **VN**, **NbN**, **TaN**, **Mo_2N**, **W_2N**, **UN**, **U_2N_3**, **Mn_5N_2**, **Mn_3N_2**. The nitrides whose formulas are given in regular type are examples of the so-called ionic nitrides; they all contain N^{3-} ions (~ 1.4-Å radius) in their crystal lattices.

The nitrides with formulas in italics are *covalent* nitrides. Boron nitride is a giant molecule with a graphite-like structure. The other group III nitrides all have the wurtzite structure, which is very much like that of diamond. It will be noted that a group III atom and a nitrogen atom are isoelectronic with two carbon atoms.

The nitrides with formulas in boldface type are *interstitial* or *metallic* nitrides. These have expanded metal lattices in which nitrogen atoms occupy interstitial positions. It is thus understandable that these interstitial nitrides have variable composition and are often nonstoichiometric.

Table 3-8 *Properties of interstitial nitrides*

	ΔH_f°, kcal/g-atom of N, 25°C	Melting point, °K	Density	Hardness, Mohs' scale[a]
TiN	−80.7	3200	5.4	8–9
ZrN	−87.3	3255	7.3	8+
HfN	−78.3	3580		
VN	−40.8	2320	6.1	9–10
NbN	−59	Dec. 2320	7.3	8+
TaN	−58.1	3360		8+
Cr_2N	−26.3			
CrN	−28.3	Dec. 1770	6.1	
Mo_2N	−16.6			
W_2N	−17			
ThN		2900		
UN	−80	2900	14.3	
U_2N_3	−71	Dec.	11.2	

[a] 8 = topaz; 9 = ruby, sapphire; 10 = diamond.

The interstitial nitrides usually have high melting points, extreme hardness, metallic conductivity, and relatively high chemical inertness.   Some properties of such nitrides are listed in Table 3-8.   Very pure, crystalline nitrides of Ti, Zr, Hf, V, Nb, and Ta can be deposited on incandescent tungsten filaments in mixtures of nitrogen, hydrogen, and the appropriate metal chloride vapor.

$$2TiCl_4 + N_2 + 4H_2 \rightarrow 2TiN + 8HCl$$

Reaction temperatures of 1100 to 1700° are used.

3-7   AMMONIA HYDRATES AND AQUEOUS AMMONIA

Above 0°, ammonia and water are miscible in all proportions. The freezing point–composition curve for the system H_2O–NH_3 is given in Fig. 3-6.   The two pronounced maxima in the phase diagram indicate the existence of two ammonia hydrates, the monohydrate or ammonium hydroxide and the hemihydrate or ammonium oxide.   Evidence has been found for a dihydrate that melts incongruently at $-98°$ in the region of the eutectic between ice and ammonia monohydrate.   The monohydrate melts at $-79.0°$ and the hemihydrate at $-78.8°$.

The crystal structure of the hemihydrate consists of a three-

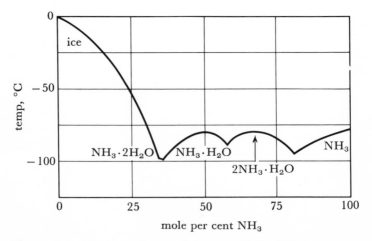

Figure 3-6   *The phase diagram of the system H_2O—NH_3.*

dimensional network of alternating nitrogen and oxygen atoms connected by hydrogen bonds. Half of the ammonia molecules are not part of the network, but are attached to it each by a single hydrogen bond. Except for the hydrogen atoms of the latter ammonia molecules, all the hydrogen atoms are involved in hydrogen bonds. The lone pair of each nitrogen atom is used in a single hydrogen bond, and the two lone pairs of each oxygen atom are used in three hydrogen bonds.

The crystal structure of the monohydrate contains water molecules hydrogen-bonded to each other into planar chains. These chains are cross-linked into a three-dimensional network by ammonia molecules. The ammonia molecules are not bonded to themselves. One of the lone pairs of each oxygen atom is used in a single hydrogen bond, and the other lone pair is used for three weak hydrogen bonds. The lone pair of each nitrogen atom is used in a single hydrogen bond.

The low-temperature heat-capacity curve of $NH_3 \cdot \frac{1}{2}H_2O$ shows two maxima in the neighborhood of 52°K. This transition region probably corresponds to the onset of rotation for the ammonia molecules in the lattice that are not an integral part of the three-dimensional network.

The densities and partial pressures of ammonia over aqueous ammonia solutions at 20° are given in Table 3-9. At ordinary concentrations, a small fraction of the dissolved ammonia reacts with water as follows:

$$NH_3 + H_2O = NH_4^+ + OH^-$$

Table 3-9   *Densities and partial pressures of ammonia of aqueous ammonia solutions, 20°*

Weight % NH_3	Molarity	Density	NH_3 pressure, mm Hg
1	0.584	0.9939	
2	1.162	0.9895	12.5
4	2.304	0.9811	26.1
8	4.534	0.9651	60
16	8.796	0.9362	156
28	14.76	0.8980	447

Table 3-10   *Ionization constants for aqueous ammonia*

Temp, °C	$K_b \times 10^5$	Temp, °C	$K_b \times 10^5$
0	1.374	20	1.710
5	1.479	25	1.774
10	1.570	30	1.820
15	1.652	35	1.849

Equilibrium constants for this basic ionization are given for various temperatures in Table 3-10.   The reaction has a forward rate constant of $\sim 5 \times 10^5$ sec^{-1} and a reverse rate constant of $\sim 3 \times 10^{10}$ liters mole^{-1} sec^{-1}.

High field conductance measurements and solvent extraction studies suggest that the nonionized ammonia in aqueous ammonia exists in two forms, a hydrated form and an unhydrated form, although there is some question as to the interpretation of the data. It has been suggested that the following equilibria are involved in aqueous ammonia solutions:

$$NH_3 + H_2O = NH_3 \cdot H_2O \qquad K \sim 0.21$$

$$NH_3 \cdot H_2O = NH_4^+ + OH^- \qquad K \sim 8.6 \times 10^{-5}$$

There seems to be no good reason for considering the hydrated form as "ammonium hydroxide." There are three conceivable configurations for the hydrated form: $NH_4^+ \cdots OH^-$, H_2N—$H \cdots OH_2$, and $H_3N \cdots H$—OH. The very small shift in the $3\nu_1$ harmonic N—H vibration frequency between gaseous ammonia (9688 cm^{-1}) and aqueous ammonia (9676 cm^{-1}) indicates that the last configuration is realized.   Nmr studies have shown that the mean lifetime of the $N \cdots H$—O hydrogen bond is 2×10^{-12} sec.

3-8   AMMONIUM SALTS

Ammonia reacts with protonic acids to form ammonium salts. Since the ammonium ion has about the same radius (1.43 Å) as the potassium ion and rubidium ion, ammonium salts and potassium or rubidium salts are often isomorphous.   And, like potassium and rubidium salts, ammonium salts are usually quite soluble in water.

However, the perchlorate, hydrogen tartrate, hexanitrocobaltate-(III), and hexachloroplatinate(IV) salts are only slightly soluble.

At elevated temperatures most ammonium salts dissociate to gaseous ammonia and the corresponding protonic acid. For example,

$$NH_4Cl(s) = NH_3(g) + HCl(g)$$

$$(NH_4)_2SO_4(s) = NH_3(g) + (NH_4)HSO_4(s)$$

$$NH_4HS(s) = NH_3(g) + H_2S(g)$$

In general, the most stable ammonium salts are those with large uninegative anions. Small or highly charged anions polarize the ammonium ion so that the salt readily dissociates to free ammonia and the free acid. The dissociation pressures of some ammonium salts are plotted in Fig. 3-7.

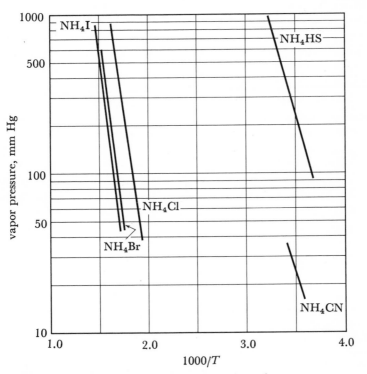

Figure 3-7 *Vapor pressures of some ammonium salts.*

When ammonium salts with oxidizing anions are heated, an irreversible reaction occurs in which an oxidation product of ammonia (nitrogen or a nitrogen oxide) is formed. The principal net decomposition reactions for ammonium nitrite and ammonium nitrate are given below.

$$NH_4NO_2 \rightarrow N_2 + 2H_2O$$

$$NH_4NO_3 \rightarrow N_2O + 2H_2O$$

The aqueous ammonium ion is completely oxidized to nitrogen and nitrogen oxides by a hot mixture of nitric and hydrochloric acids. This reaction is very useful in analysis when it is necessary to completely eliminate the ammonium ion from a solution.

The ammonium ion is isoelectronic with the borohydride ion and the methane molecule. In each case, the four hydrogen atoms are at the corners of a regular tetrahedron (sp^3 hybridization). The bond distances for these species are B—H, 1.25 Å; C—H, 1.09 Å; N—H, 1.03 Å. The trend is what one might expect on the basis of the electronegativity differences ($\Delta x = 0.1, 0.4$, and 0.9, respectively) or the trend in atomic radii among the first-row elements. In common with the alkali borohydrides and methane, many ammonium salts exhibit lambda points, or maxima in the heat capacity–temperature curves. For ammonium salts, the lambda points generally occur in the temperature interval from room temperature to $-70°$, the exact temperature of the maximum depending on the salt. The lambda points for several salts are given in Table 3-11. It is believed that these points correspond to transitions in which restricted rotations of the ammonium ions become free upon absorbing the additional energy corresponding to the extra area under the heat capacity–temperature curve.

Table 3-11   *Lambda points for ammonium salts*

Salt	Lambda point, °C	Salt	Lambda point, °C
NH_4Cl	-30.5	$(NH_4)_3AsO_4 \cdot 3H_2O$	-56.0
NH_4Br	-38.1	$(NH_4)_2Cr_2O_7$	-2.4
NH_4I	-41.6	$NH_4H_2PO_4$	$+18.9$
$(NH_4)_2SO_4$	-49.7		

The lambda points have been found to correspond to the temperatures below which the ammonium salts become ferroelectric or antiferroelectric.

3-9 AMMONIUM AMALGAMS

Solutions of ammonium (NH_4) in mercury, usually called ammonium amalgams, may be prepared either by the electrolysis of a cold ammonium salt solution using a mercury cathode or by the treatment of an ammonium salt solution with an alkali-metal amalgam. Ammonium amalgams are unstable at room temperature, decomposing to ammonia and hydrogen.

$$NH_4(Hg_x) \rightarrow NH_3 + \tfrac{1}{2}H_2 + xHg$$

While decomposing, the amalgam is a voluminous spongy mass because of the bubbles of gas being evolved. Amalgams of substituted ammoniums such as $(CH_3)_4N$, CH_3NH_3, and $(CH_3)_2NH_2$ may be prepared by exactly analogous procedures using solutions of the corresponding substituted ammonium salts. Tetramethylammonium amalgam decomposes to trimethylamine, methane, and ethylene.

In the electrolysis of a tetraalkyl ammonium salt solution in liquid ammonia, using a platinum cathode, electrons pass from the cathode into the solution. Thus, in the cathode compartment one may prepare an ammonia solution of a tetraalkyl ammonium. Since the solution contains the species R_4N^+ and e^-, its behavior is quite analogous to that of an alkali-metal solution.

Tetramethylammonium decomposes in ammonia to give trimethylamine, methane, and methylamine. Higher homologs such as tetraethylammonium decompose to give the tertiary amine, olefin, and alkane.

3-10 AMMONIATES AND AMMINES

Many metal salts form ammonia addition compounds, which are structurally analogous to hydrates. In most of these ammoniates the ammonia molecules are clustered around the metal ions, presumably with the protons of the ammonia molecules directed away from the metal ion. Naturally, the most stable ammoniates are formed by salts containing metal ions that are small or highly charged. A few examples of labile ammoniates

Table 3-12 *Some ammoniated salts and their dissociation pressures at 25°*

Salt	P, cm Hg	Salt	P, cm Hg
$CaCl_2 \cdot 8NH_3$		$LiCl \cdot 4NH_3$	
$CaCl_2 \cdot 4NH_3$	115	$LiCl \cdot 3NH_3$	132
$CaCl_2 \cdot 2NH_3$	29	$LiCl \cdot 2NH_3$	11.2
		$LiCl$	1.7
$CaBR_2 \cdot 8NH_3$			
$CaBr_2 \cdot 6NH_3$	69		
$CaBr_2 \cdot 2NH_3$	1.9	$LiBr \cdot 5NH_3$	
$CaBr_2 \cdot NH_3$	0.0019	$LiBr \cdot 4NH_3$	1180
$CaBr_2$	0.000085	$LiBr \cdot 3NH_3$	12
$BaBr_2 \cdot 8NH_3$		$LiI \cdot 5NH_3$	
$BaBr_2 \cdot 4NH_3$	42	$LiI \cdot 4NH_3$	740
		$LiI \cdot 3NH_3$	1.4
$FeCl_2 \cdot 6NH_3$	0.59	$LiI \cdot 2NH_3$	1.2
$FeCl_2 \cdot 2NH_3$	0.000023	$LiI \cdot NH_3$	0.091
$FeCl_2 \cdot NH_3$	7.8×10^{-8}		
$FeCl_2$		$NaI \cdot 4.5NH_3$	36
		NaI	
$NiCl_2 \cdot 6NH_3$	0.020		
$NiCl_2 \cdot 2NH_3$	0.000013	$CuSO_4 \cdot 5NH_3$	1.05
$NiCl_2 \cdot NH_3$		$CuSO_4 \cdot 4NH_3$	0.024
$MnCl_2 \cdot 6NH_3$	2.5	$CuSO_4 \cdot 2NH_3$	0.000017
$MnCl_2 \cdot 2NH_3$	0.00050	$CuSO_4 \cdot NH_3$	
$MnCl_2 \cdot NH_3$			

are given in Table 3-12.   Each of these ammoniates may be converted to the next lowest ammoniate or to the unammoniated salt by either pumping or heating.   The equilibrium ammonia vapor pressures at 25° over the ammoniates are given in the table.

In aqueous solution, many metal ions react with ammonia to form ammoniated ions that are often called ammine complexes. The best known example is the silver ammine complex, $Ag(NH_3)_2^+$. The over-all equilibrium constant (β_2) for the formation of this complex from Ag^+ and $2NH_3$ has the value 1.70×10^7 at 25°.

Table 3-13 *Successive formation constants for aqueous metal ammines*

Metal ion	Temp, °C	$\log_{10}$ of					
		K_1	K_2	K_3	K_4	K_5	K_6
$\mathrm{Li^+}$	23	-0.3	-0.8	-1.3			
$\mathrm{Mg^{2+}}$	23	0.23	-0.15	-0.42	-0.7	-0.95	-1.3
$\mathrm{Ca^{2+}}$	23	-0.2	-0.6	-0.8	-1.1	-1.3	-1.7
$\mathrm{Fe^{2+}}$	25	$\log \beta_4 \sim 3.7$					
$\mathrm{Co^{2+}}$	30	1.99	1.51	0.93	0.64	0.06	-0.74
							$\log \beta_6 = 4.39$
$\mathrm{Co^{3+}}$	30	7.3	6.7	6.1	5.6	5.05	4.41
							$\log \beta_6 = 35.21$
$\mathrm{Ni^{2+}}$	30	2.67	2.12	1.61	1.07	0.63	-0.09
							$\log \beta_6 = 8.01$
$\mathrm{Cu^+}$	18	5.93	4.93	$\log \beta_2 = 10.86$			
$\mathrm{Cu^{2+}}$	30	3.99	3.34	2.73	1.97	$\log \beta_4 = 12.03$	
$\mathrm{Ag^+}$	25	3.315	3.915	$\log \beta_2 = 7.23$			
$\mathrm{Zn^{2+}}$	30	2.18	2.25	2.31	1.96	$\log \beta_4 = 8.70$	
$\mathrm{Cd^{2+}}$	30	2.51	1.96	1.30	0.79	$\log \beta_4 = 6.56$	
$\mathrm{Hg^{2+}}$	22	8.8	8.7	1.00	0.78	$\log \beta_4 = 19.3$	
$\mathrm{Tl^+}$	22.5	-0.9					

However, the reaction proceeds in two steps, for each of which the formation constants are known:

$$\mathrm{Ag^+ + NH_3 = AgNH_3^+} \qquad K_1 = 2.06 \times 10^3$$

$$\mathrm{AgNH_3^+ + NH_3 = Ag(NH_3)_2^+} \qquad K_2 = 8.2 \times 10^3$$

The logarithms of the successive formation constants for a wide variety of metal ammines are given in Table 3-13. (β_n is defined as follows: $\beta_n = K_1 \cdot K_2 \cdots K_n$.)

Trisilylamine

One of the most fascinating amines (substituted ammonias) is the compound trisilylamine, $\mathrm{(SiH_3)_3N}$, which may be prepared by the reaction between excess silyl chloride and ammonia:

$$\mathrm{3SiH_3Cl + 4NH_3 \rightarrow (SiH_3)_3N + 3NH_4Cl}$$

This molecule is particularly significant because it exhibits practically no basic properties. Thus it does not form an adduct with either $\mathrm{BH_3}$ or $\mathrm{B(CH_3)_3}$, as does the corresponding carbon compound, trimethylamine. With hydrogen chloride, decomposition to silyl chloride takes place:

$$\mathrm{(SiH_3)_3N + 4HCl \rightarrow 3SiH_3Cl + NH_4Cl}$$

At $-78°$, boron trichloride reacts to form a compound of composition $(SiH_3)_3N \cdot BCl_3$, but the material readily decomposes to form SiH_3Cl and $(SiH_3)_2NBCl_2$.

From simple electronegativity considerations, one would have predicted that trisilylamine would be more basic than trimethylamine. In order to explain the peculiar behavior of trisilylamine, A. B. Burg suggested that the lone pair of electrons on the nitrogen atom is engaged in internal dative bonding to the vacant $3d$ orbitals of the silicon atoms, and he correctly predicted that the Si_3N skeleton is planar. It may be that steric repulsion can equally well account for the planarity and weak basicity of the molecule.

REFERENCES

L. F. Audrieth and J. Kleinberg, *Non-Aqueous Solvents*, Wiley, New York, 1953.

W. L. Jolly, "Metal-ammonia solutions," *Progr. Inorg. Chem.*, **1** (**1959**), 235.

E. C. Franklin, *The Nitrogen System of Compounds*, Reinhold, New York, 1935.

F. W. Bergstrom and W. C. Fernelius, "Chemistry of alkali amides," *Chem. Rev.*, **12**, 43 (1933); **20**, 413 (1937); R. Levine and W. C. Fernelius, *ibid.*, **54**, 449 (1954).

P. Schwarzkopf and R. Kieffer, *Refractory Hard Metals*, pp. 223–260 (Interstitial nitrides), Macmillan, New York, 1953.

E. Arnold, H. Freitag, and A. Patterson, Jr., in W. Hamer (ed.), *Structure of Electrolytic Solutions*, Chap. 18, p. 281 (High-field conductance of aqueous ammonia), Wiley, New York, 1959.

R. G. Bates and G. D. Pinching, "Ionization constant of aqueous ammonia," *J. Am. Chem. Soc.*, **72**, 1393 (1950).

I. Olovsson and D. H. Templeton, *Acta Cryst.*, "Crystal structures of ammonia and ammonia hydrates," **12**, 827, 832 (1959); W. J. Siemons and D. H. Templeton, *ibid.*, **7**, 194 (1954).

A. B. Hart and J. R. Partington, "Vapor pressures over ammoniates," *J. Chem. Soc.*, **1943**, 104.

J. Bjerrum, G. Schwarzenbach, and L. G. Sillén, "Stability constants: Part II, Inorganic ligands," *Chem. Soc.* (*London*), *Spec. Publ.* **7** (**1958**).

4

Nitrogen-Halogen Compounds

4-1 NITROGEN-FLUORINE COMPOUNDS

Nitrogen Fluorides

Five binary nitrogen-fluorine compounds have been prepared: nitrogen trifluoride, NF_3; tetrafluorohydrazine, N_2F_4; two isomers (cis and trans) of difluorodiazine, N_2F_2; and azine fluoride, N_3F.

Nitrogen trifluoride is an odorless, colorless gas at room temperature; its boiling and melting points are $-129.01°$ and $-206.79°$, respectively. The material is prepared by the electrolysis of molten anhydrous ammonium bifluoride or of solutions of ammonium bifluoride in anhydrous hydrogen fluoride. Nitrogen trifluoride is also formed in the direct fluorination of ammonia:

$$4NH_3 + 3F_2 \rightarrow NF_3 + 3NH_4F$$

Electron diffraction studies indicate that the NF_3 molecule is pyramidal with an F—N—F bond angle of $102.5°$ and an N—F bond distance of 1.37 Å. The molecule possesses a remarkably low dipole moment of 0.234 Debye unit. It is interesting to note that, although the bond angle in NF_3 is more acute than the bond

47

angle in NH_3 and although the N—F bond is more polar than the N—H bond, the dipole moment of NF_3 is much smaller than that of NH_3 (1.47 Debye unit).   We may explain this apparent anomaly in terms of the large moment of the lone pair of electrons on the nitrogen atom.   In NH_3, the lone-pair–nitrogen moment is so oriented that it adds to the nitrogen-hydrogen moment.   Thus ammonia has a large dipole moment.   However, in NF_3, the lone-pair–nitrogen moment is so oriented that it cancels the fluorine-nitrogen moment.   Thus nitrogen trifluoride has a small dipole moment.   Reference to Figure 4-1 will make this clear.

Nitrogen trifluoride is a remarkably unreactive material, which is in part attributable to its thermodynamic stability with respect to the elements.   The heat and free energy of formation (ΔH_f° and ΔF_f°) of NF_3 are -29.7 and -19.7 kcal/mole, respectively.   Nitrogen trifluoride is unaffected by water and dilute aqueous alkali and acid.   It seems to have no basic properties whatsoever.   Mixtures with various species such as water vapor, ammonia, hydrogen, methane, ethylene, carbon monoxide, and hydrogen sulfide undergo reaction when sparked.   For example, water reacts under these conditions as follows:

$$2NF_3 + 3H_2O \rightarrow 6HF + NO + NO_2$$

Tetrafluorohydrazine may be prepared by heating NF_3 in the presence of various reducing agents such as stainless steel,

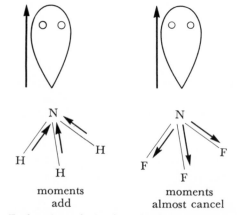

moments   moments
add   almost cancel

Figure 4-1   *Explanation of the low dipole moment of NF_3.   Arrows indicate the direction from $+$ to $-$.*

copper, arsenic, antimony, and bismuth. The best yields have been obtained by using a flow reactor packed with copper turnings at 375°. The melting and boiling points for N_2F_4 are $-168°$ and $-73°$, respectively.

Tetrafluorohydrazine dissociates into spectrometrically detectable amounts of NF_2 radicals even at room temperature:

$$N_2F_4 = 2NF_2$$

At elevated temperatures, the dissociation can be detected by pressure measurements. Thus, at 150°, $K = 0.03$. When N_2F_4 is frozen out from the cold gas at relatively high pressures, the solid is colorless; when frozen out from the hot gas at low pressures, the solid is dark blue. The color is attributed to the radical NF_2. As might be expected, N_2F_4 participates in a variety of free-radical reactions. N_2F_4 and chlorine react in ultraviolet light to form chlorodifluoramine:

$$Cl_2 + N_2F_4 \rightarrow 2ClNF_2$$

N_2F_4 and nitric oxide react to form nitrosodifluoramine:

$$N_2F_4 + 2NO \rightarrow 2NF_2NO$$

Diketones react under ultraviolet irradiation to give N,N-difluoramides

$$\underset{\substack{\| \\ RC}}{O}\underset{\substack{\| \\ CR}}{O} + N_2F_4 \rightarrow 2RCONF_2$$

Such compounds may also be prepared by the reaction of aldehydes with N_2F_4:

$$CH_3CHO + N_2F_4 \rightarrow CH_3CONF_2 + HNF_2$$

Difluorodiazine, N_2F_2, is a minor gaseous product from the electrolysis of molten ammonium bifluoride. The N_2F_2 obtained is a mixture of two isomers, a trans form (bp $-111.4°$, mp $-172°$) and a cis form (bp $-105.7°$, mp $< -195°$), although it is barely possible that the cis form is really 1,1-difluorodiazine, $F_2N{=}N$. The cis isomer is much more reactive than the trans isomer. Thus the cis isomer reacts completely in two weeks with glass to form SiF_4 and N_2O, whereas the trans isomer is unchanged after a month.

Azine fluoride, N_3F, is one of the gaseous products of the reaction of fluorine with nitrogen-diluted hydrogen azide. It is a very explosive material with boiling and melting points of $-82°$ and $-154°$, respectively. The structure of this material is unknown.

Fluoramines

Difluoramine, HNF_2, is a very unstable, explosive material (bp $-23.6°$) that may be made by the reaction of tetrafluorohydrazine with thiophenol and other mercaptans:

$$N_2F_4 + C_6H_5SH \rightarrow 2HNF_2 + C_6H_5SSC_6H_5$$

Difluoramine may be reduced quantitatively by aqueous hydriodic acid:

$$HNF_2 + 4H^+ + 6I^- \rightarrow 2I_3^- + NH_4^+ + HF + F^-$$

Monofluoramine has been reported as a by-product of the electrolysis of molten ammonium bifluoride, but the data are unconfirmed.

Nitrogen Oxyfluorides

Nitrosyl fluoride, NOF, may be prepared by the reaction of nitric oxide with fluorine.

$$2NO + F_2 \rightarrow 2NOF$$

The reaction is believed to proceed by the following mechanism:

$$F_2 + NO \rightarrow NOF + F \quad \text{(rate-determining)}$$

$$F + NO \rightleftharpoons NOF^* \rightarrow NOF + h\nu$$
$$\underset{(M)}{\big\downarrow} NOF$$

The F—N=O molecule is V-shaped, with a bond angle of $110.2°$, an N—F distance of 1.52 Å, and an N—O distance of 1.13 Å.   If sp^2 hybrid orbitals of the nitrogen atom were used in forming the σ bonds to the fluorine and oxygen atoms, one would expect a bond angle of $120°$.   Apparently the lone pair of electrons strongly repels the bonding electrons and causes the bond angle to decrease to $110°$.

Although nitrosyl fluoride is far less reactive than elementary fluorine, it reacts readily with many elements to form fluorides and either nitric oxide or nitrogen dioxide.   Nitrosyl fluoride reacts with a variety of fluorides to form salt-like addition compounds such as $NOAsF_6$, $NOVF_6$, and $NOBF_4$. These compounds are best regarded as salts containing the nitrosyl cation, NO^+.

Nitryl fluoride, NO_2F, may be prepared by the reaction of nitrogen dioxide with fluorine:

$$2NO_2 + F_2 \rightarrow 2NO_2F$$

The reaction is believed to proceed by the following mechanism:

$$F_2 + NO_2 \rightarrow NO_2F + F \qquad \text{(rate-determining)}$$
$$F + NO_2 + M \rightarrow NO_2F + M$$

The F—NO_2 molecule is planar, with an N—F bond distance of 1.35 Å and an N—O bond distance of 1.23 Å.

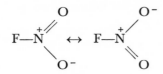

In a purely formal way, a molecule of nitryl fluoride may be looked upon as a molecule of nitrosyl fluoride in which the lone pair on the nitrogen atom is used to form a bond to an oxygen atom.

Most metals react with nitryl fluoride to form both the metal fluoride and the metal oxide:

$$Zn + 2NO_2F \rightarrow 2NO_2 + ZnF_2$$
$$Zn + NO_2 \rightarrow ZnO + NO$$

Chromium, molybdenum, tungsten, and uranium form oxy-fluorides:

$$2NO_2F + M \rightarrow 2NO + MO_2F_2$$

Almost all nonmetals react with nitryl fluoride to form nitryl salts such as NO_2PF_6, NO_2SbF_6, and NO_2BF_4.

Nitrogen-Fluorine-Chlorine Compounds

Chlorodifluoramine, NF_2Cl, and dichlorofluoramine, $NFCl_2$, are extremely reactive compounds with boiling points of -67 and $-3°$, respectively. NF_2Cl is formed in a little-characterized reaction between HNF_2 and BCl_3. $NFCl_2$ has been prepared by the reaction of chlorine fluoride with sodium azide:

$$NaN_3 + 2ClF \rightarrow NaF + N_2 + NFCl_2$$

Inasmuch as chlorine azide has also been observed to react with chlorine fluoride to give $NFCl_2$, it is suspected that the above reaction proceeds in two steps:

$$NaN_3 + ClF \rightarrow ClN_3 + NaF$$

$$ClN_3 + ClF \rightarrow N_2 + NFCl_2$$

4-2 NITROGEN-CHLORINE COMPOUNDS

Nitrogen Trichloride and Chloramines

Aqueous solutions of chloramine, NH_2Cl, are prepared by the reaction of aqueous ammonia and hypochlorite solutions:

$$NH_3 + OCl^- = NH_2Cl + OH^-$$

The equilibrium constant for this reaction is not known, but it is believed to be greater than 10^8. If a solution of chloramine is acidified, dichloramine and finally nitrogen trichloride are formed:

$$H^+ + 2NH_2Cl = NHCl_2 + NH_4^+ \qquad K \sim 10^6$$

$$H^+ + 3NHCl_2 = 2NCl_3 + NH_4^+ \qquad K \sim 10^4$$

Nitrogen trichloride is an oily liquid which is soluble in organic solvents such as carbon tetrachloride and benzene. Solutions of NCl_3 in such solvents may be obtained by extraction from aqueous solutions. An aqueous solution of NCl_3 is conveniently prepared by the passage of chlorine into an ammonium salt solution. Nitrogen trichloride is explosive, a property consistent with its positive heat of formation, $\Delta H_f^\circ = 55$ kcal/mole.

Chloramine decomposes to nitrogen and ammonia in alkaline solution:

$$3NH_2Cl + 3OH^- \rightarrow N_2 + 3Cl^- + NH_3 + 3H_2O$$

It has been shown that hydroxylamine is an intermediate in the reaction, and it is believed that the first step is the nucleophilic substitution

$$NH_2Cl + OH^- \rightarrow NH_2OH + Cl^-$$

although one cannot rule out the possibility of a reaction sequence such as the following:

$$NH_2Cl + OH^- = NHCl^- + H_2O \qquad \text{(fast equilibrium)}$$

$$NHCl^- + H_2O \rightarrow NH_2OH + Cl^- \qquad \text{(rate-determining)}$$

The final products are formed by the relatively fast reaction

$$NH_2Cl + 2NH_2OH + OH^- \rightarrow N_2 + NH_3 + 3H_2O + Cl^-$$

Chloramine is an important intermediate in the reaction of hypochlorite with ammonia to form hydrazine (see Section 5-1).

Chloramine vapor, mixed with large amounts of gaseous ammonia, may be easily prepared by passing chlorine gas into a stream of excess ammonia gas.

$$Cl_2 + 2NH_3 \rightarrow NH_2Cl + NH_4Cl$$

The ammonium chloride may be filtered out and the product stream of gas may be used to effect a variety of "chloramination" reactions. For example, 1,1,1-trisubstituted hydrazonium chlorides may be prepared from tertiary amines, and amino-phosphonium chlorides may be prepared from trisubstituted phosphines.

$$R_3N + NH_2Cl \rightarrow [R_3NNH_2]Cl$$

$$R_3P + NH_2Cl \rightarrow [R_3PNH_2]Cl$$

Nitrogen Oxychlorides

Nitrosyl chloride (mp $-64.5°$, bp $-6.4°$) is an orange-yellow gas which may be prepared by the reaction of chlorine and nitric oxide

$$2NO + Cl_2 = 2NOCl$$

The reaction is kinetically third order,

$$\frac{d[NOCl]}{dt} = k[NO]^2[Cl_2]$$

and it has been presumed that the $(NO)_2$ molecule is formed as an intermediate, even though such a species has never been directly observed.

$$2NO \rightleftharpoons (NO)_2 \qquad \text{(rapid equilibrium)}$$

$$(NO)_2 + Cl_2 \rightarrow 2NOCl \qquad \text{(rate-determining)}$$

Nitrosyl chloride may be more conveniently prepared by passing N_2O_4 over moist KCl at room temperature:

$$N_2O_4 + KCl \rightarrow NOCl + KNO_3$$

The molecule Cl—N=O has a Cl—N—O bond angle of 116°, an N—Cl bond distance of 1.95 Å, and an N—O bond distance of 1.14 Å.

Nitryl chloride (mp $-145°$, bp $-15.9°$) is a colorless gas that can be prepared by the reaction of chlorosulfonic acid with anhydrous nitric acid,

$$ClSO_3H + HNO_3 \rightarrow NO_2Cl + H_2SO_4$$

or by the passage of hydrogen chloride through a solution of nitric acid in sulfuric acid,

$$HCl + NO_2^+ + HSO_4^- \rightarrow NO_2Cl + H_2SO_4$$

(HNO_3 reacts with $2H_2SO_4$ to form $NO_2^+ + H_3O^+ + 2HSO_4^-$.) The Cl—$NO_2$ molecule is planar, with an N—Cl bond distance of 1.79 Å and an N—O bond distance of 1.24 Å.

Nitryl chloride reacts with water to form hydrochloric acid and nitric acid,

$$NO_2Cl + H_2O \rightarrow 2H^+ + NO_3^- + Cl^-$$

but the analogous reaction with ammonia yields chloramine and ammonium nitrite,

$$NO_2Cl + 2NH_3 \rightarrow NH_2Cl + NH_4NO_2$$

This apparent discrepancy is explained by assuming that the ammonia-type cleavage (in which NO_2Cl reacts as if it were $NO_2^- + Cl^+$) is normal and that the initial step in water is to form HOCl and HNO_2. However, these latter species rapidly react to form chloride and nitrate:

$$HOCl + HNO_2 \rightarrow NO_3^- + Cl^- + 2H^+$$

4-3 NITROGEN-BROMINE COMPOUNDS

Bromine reacts with liquid ammonia to form a solution of bromamine:

$$Br_2 + 2NH_3 \rightarrow NH_2Br + NH_4^+ + Br^-$$

By evaporation of the solvent ammonia, one obtains a reddish-violet solid of composition $NBr_3 \cdot 6NH_3$ (or $3NH_2Br \cdot 4NH_3$) which decomposes explosively when warmed to room temperature. NH_2Br and $NHBr_2$ may be prepared by the interaction of bromine and ammonia in ether solution at low temperatures, but the compounds have never been isolated.

Nitrosyl bromide, NOBr, may be prepared by mixing nitric oxide and bromine:

$$2NO + Br_2 = 2NOBr$$

The pure compound cannot be prepared, inasmuch as it decomposes reversibly to NO and Br_2. At room temperature it is about 7 per cent decomposed at 1 atm pressure of NOBr. The boiling point is approximately $0°$. Nitrosyl bromide has the structure Br—N=O, with a bond angle of $117°$, an N—Br bond distance of 2.14 Å, and an N—O bond distance of 1.15 Å.

Nitryl bromide has never been prepared.

4-4 NITROGEN-IODINE COMPOUNDS

It is believed that aqueous solutions of ammonia and iodine are in equilibrium with iodamine, NH_2I:

$$2NH_3 + I_2 = NH_2I + NH_4^+ + I^-$$

An equilibrium constant of 1.8 has been reported for the reaction. At sufficiently high concentrations of iodine, black $NI_3 \cdot NH_3$ precipitates:

$$NH_2I + 2I_2 + 3NH_3 = 2NH_4^+ + 2I^- + NI_3 \cdot NH_3(s)$$

The latter compound will dissolve in excess of ammonia solution:

$$NI_3 \cdot NH_3(s) + NH_3 = 3NH_2I$$

$NI_3 \cdot NH_3$ is a shock- and light-sensitive compound that decomposes explosively to nitrogen, iodine, and ammonia.

REFERENCES

M. Anbar and G. Yagil, " The hydrolysis of chloramine in alkaline solution," *J. Am. Chem. Soc.*, **84**, 1790 (1962).

C. J. Hoffman and R. G. Neville, "Nitrogen fluorides," *Chem. Rev.*, **62**, 1 (1962).

D. M. Yost and H. Russell, Jr., *Systematic Inorganic Chemistry*, Prentice-Hall, Englewood Cliffs, N.J., 1946.

5

The Hydronitrogens and
Hydroxylamine

5-1 HYDRAZINE, N_2H_4

Preparation

The commercial method for preparing hydrazine is the same as that used by Raschig in 1907. The over-all reaction, which is carried out in aqueous solution, is

$$2NH_3 + OCl^- \rightarrow N_2H_4 + Cl^- + H_2O$$

but the reaction proceeds in two main steps. In the first step, discussed in Section 4-2, chloramine is formed,

$$NH_3 + OCl^- \rightarrow OH^- + NH_2Cl$$

and the chloramine then reacts with ammonia to form hydrazine:

$$NH_3 + NH_2Cl + OH^- \rightarrow N_2H_4 + Cl^- + H_2O$$

The following side reaction prevents the hydrazine from forming in 100 per cent yield:

$$2NH_2Cl + N_2H_4 \rightarrow N_2 + 2NH_4^+ + 2Cl^-$$

This hydrazine-destroying reaction is catalyzed by traces of ions of heavy metals like copper. In order to sequester such metal ions (and also probably somehow to catalyze the hydrazine-forming reaction), gelatin or glue is usually added to the reaction mixture. Large excesses of ammonia are usually employed in order to favor the chloramine-ammonia reaction over the chloramine-hydrazine reaction. Distillation of the resulting dilute solution of hydrazine yields a 58.5 per cent hydrazine-41.5 per cent water azeotropic solution which may be concentrated to anhydrous N_2H_4 by distillation over sodium hydroxide. Alternatively, the addition of sulfuric acid to the dilute hydrazine solution causes the precipitation of hydrazine sulfate, $N_2H_6SO_4$.

It has been demonstrated that the reaction of chloramine with ammonia proceeds by two independent paths, a base-independent path and a base-catalyzed path. The base-independent path is believed to be the nucleophilic attack of ammonia on chloramine:

$$NH_3 + NH_2Cl \rightarrow N_2H_5^+ + Cl^- \qquad \text{(slow)}$$
$$N_2H_5^+ + OH^- = N_2H_4 + H_2O \qquad \text{(fast)}$$

The base-catalyzed path is believed to involve the preliminary formation of the chloramide ion, followed by attack on this ion by ammonia:

$$NH_2Cl + OH^- = NHCl^- + H_2O \qquad \text{(fast)}$$
$$NH_3 + NHCl^- \rightarrow N_2H_4 + Cl^- \qquad \text{(slow)}$$

The irradiation of gaseous ammonia with high-energy particles such as deuterons may be a commercially feasible method for preparing hydrazine. The irradiation is believed to yield amide radicals, which combine to form hydrazine:

$$2NH_2 \rightarrow N_2H_4$$

These radicals are probably formed in the following reaction sequence:

$$NH_3 \xrightarrow{\text{irradiation}} NH_3^+ + e^-$$
$$NH_3^+ + NH_3 \rightarrow NH_4^+ + NH_2$$
$$NH_4^+ + e^- \rightarrow NH_2 + H_2$$

Atomic hydrogen seems to be deleterious to hydrazine production because of the following two reactions:

$$N_2H_4 + H \rightarrow N_2H_3 + H_2$$

$$N_2H_4 + H \rightarrow NH_2 + NH_3$$

The primary source of atomic hydrogen is the reaction

$$NH_3 \xrightarrow{\text{irradiation}} NH_2^+ + H + e^-$$

The latter process may be diminished, with consequently increased yields of hydrazine, by carrying out the irradiation in the presence of krypton or xenon. Under these conditions, the ammonia receives its energy by reaction with Kr^+ and Xe^+ ions which are produced by the irradiation. Whereas the reactions

$$Kr^+ + NH_3 \rightarrow NH_3^+ + Kr$$

$$Xe^+ + NH_3 \rightarrow NH_3^+ + Xe$$

are thermodynamically possible $[I(Kr) = 14.0$ eV, $I(Xe) = 12.1$ eV, $I(NH_3) = 10.1$ eV], the reactions

$$Kr^+ + NH_3 \rightarrow NH_2^+ + H + Kr$$

$$Xe^+ + NH_3 \rightarrow NH_2^+ + H + Xe$$

are thermodynamically impossible (the appearance potential for NH_2^+ using NH_3 is 16.0 eV).

Physical Properties and Structure

Anhydrous hydrazine is a colorless hygroscopic liquid that freezes at 2° and boils at 113.5°. At 25°, its density is 1.004 g/cc, its viscosity is 0.00900 dyne-sec/cm², its dielectric constant is 51.7, its heat of formation, ΔH_f°, is +12.0 kcal/mole, and its free energy of formation, ΔF_f°, is +35.61 kcal/mole. The heat and entropy of vaporization of hydrazine at its boiling point (9760 cal/mole and 25.2 eu, respectively) indicate that the liquid is extensively hydrogen-bonded.

The large dipole moment of hydrazine (1.83 to 1.90 Debye units) rules out the trans configuration for the molecule. The structure is probably the gauche form pictures in Figure 5-1. The N—N distance in hydrazine is 1.47 Å and the N—H distance is about 1.04 Å. It is interesting to note that the N—N bond distance decreases on going to $N_2H_5^+$ (1.45 Å in N_2H_5Br) and to

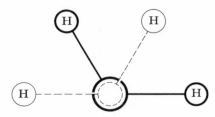

Figure 5-1   *Gauche configuration of hydrazine.*

$N_2H_6^{2+}$ (1.40 Å in $N_2H_6SO_4$).   Apparently the expected repulsion between the nitrogen atoms with $+1$ formal charges in $N_2H_6^{2+}$ is counteracted by other effects.   Probably the removal of the highly repulsive lone-pair electrons from the nitrogen atoms causes an increase in the N—N bond energy and a shortening of the N—N bond.

Chemical Properties

At room temperature, pure hydrazine and its aqueous solutions are kinetically stable with respect to decomposition.   Of course, the very positive free energy of formation of hydrazine indicates its potential instability, and, in the presence of catalytic materials such as platinum or nickel, hydrazine decomposes according to the following reactions:

$$N_2H_4 \rightarrow N_2 + 2H_2$$
$$3N_2H_4 \rightarrow N_2 + 4NH_3$$

The heat of combustion of hydrazine is enormous on either a gram or a mole basis:

$$N_2H_4(l) + O_2 \rightarrow N_2 + 2H_2O(l) \quad \Delta H° = -148.6 \text{ kcal/mole}$$

Because of this large heat of combustion and because the immediate products of combustion are gases, hydrazine, together with organo-substituted derivatives such as asymmetrical dimethylhydrazine, is used as a rocket fuel.

The hydrazine molecule may be thought of as an ammonia molecule in which one of the hydrogen atoms has been replaced by the more electronegative NH_2 group.   Consequently, hydrazine is a base, but not quite as strong as ammonia.   In aqueous solution,

$$N_2H_4 + H_2O = N_2H_5^+ + OH^- \qquad K_{25°} = 8.5 \times 10^{-7}$$
$$N_2H_5^+ + H_2O = N_2H_6^{2+} + OH^- \qquad K_{25°} \sim 9 \times 10^{-16}$$

The hydrazinium$(2+)$ ion, $N_2H_6^{2+}$, is of little importance in aqueous solutions except at extremely high acidities, but many salts of both the hydrazinium$(1+)$ ion and the hydrazinium$(2+)$ ion are known. For example, three sulfates of hydrazine are known: (1) monohydrazine sulfate (usually called "hydrazine sulfate"), $(N_2H_6)SO_4$; (2) dihydrazine sulfate, $(N_2H_5)_2SO_4$; and (3) hydrazine disulfate, $(N_2H_6)(HSO_4)_2$.

The basic character of hydrazine is shown in a wide variety of metal coordination compounds. Very little is known about the structures of these compounds. It is believed that in some compounds, such as $[Pt(NH_3)_2(N_2H_4)_2]Cl_2$, the hydrazine molecules are bonded to the metal through only one nitrogen atom. In other compounds, such as $[Pt(NO_2)_2N_2H_4]$, it is believed that the hydrazine molecule is a bidentate ligand. Of course, the latter compound may be a dinuclear complex with bridging hydrazine molecules: $(O_2N)_2Pt(NH_2NH_2)_2Pt(NO_2)_2$. Many coordination compounds containing hydrazine are only slightly soluble in water, and they may contain polymeric species in which hydrazine serves as a bridging group.

Hydrazine may be oxidized by a wide variety of oxidizing agents, including molecular oxygen. The thermodynamic reducing strength of hydrazine is dependent on the nitrogen species to which the hydrazine is oxidized. Three important half-reactions for the oxidation of hydrazine (for acid and basic solutions), together with their oxidation potentials, are given below.

For acid solutions

(1) $\quad N_2H_5^+ = N_2 + 5H^+ + 4e^- \qquad\qquad E° = +0.23$

(2) $\quad N_2H_5^+ = NH_4^+ + \frac{1}{2}N_2 + H^+ + e^- \qquad E° = +1.74$

(3) $\quad N_2H_5^+ = \frac{1}{2}HN_3 + \frac{1}{2}NH_4^+ + \frac{5}{2}H^+ + 2e^- \qquad E° = -0.11$

For basic solutions

(1′) $\quad N_2H_4 + 4OH^- = N_2 + 4H_2O + 4e^- \qquad E° = +1.16$

(2′) $\quad N_2H_4 + OH^- = NH_3 + \frac{1}{2}N_2 + H_2O + e^-$
$$E° = +2.42$$

(3′) $\quad N_2H_4 + \frac{5}{2}OH^- = \frac{1}{2}N_3^- + \frac{1}{2}NH_3 + \frac{5}{2}H_2O + 2e^-$
$$E° = +0.92$$

With some oxidizing agents, hydrazine acts as a four-electron reducing agent (as in couples 1 and 1′). For example, hydrazine is quantitatively oxidized to nitrogen gas by acid iodate, neutral iodine, and alkaline ferricyanide. One-electron oxidation of hydrazine (as in couples 2 and 2′) is approached using ferric, ceric, and permanganate. Many oxidations involve a mixture of couples 1 and 2 or 1′ and 2′. Hydrazoic acid is formed (by couples 3 and 3′) with a variety of oxidizing agents, including acidic peroxide and nitrous acid.

The oxidation of hydrazine has been studied by using hydrazine containing a nonrandom distribution of N^{15}. Under conditions in which no hydrazoic acid forms, the isotopic distribution of the molecular nitrogen that formed by four-electron oxidation (couples 1 or 1′) was the same as that of the hydrazine. One therefore concludes that both of the nitrogen atoms of each molecule of nitrogen originated in the same molecule of hydrazine. One-half of the molecular nitrogen that formed from the one-electron oxidation (couples 2 or 2′) had a random distribution of N^{15} and one-half had the same N^{15} distribution as the hydrazine. One concludes, that in the latter case, half of the nitrogen molecules contain nitrogen atoms originating from different hydrazine molecules, whereas the other half of the nitrogen molecules contain atoms originating from the same hydrazine molecules. These observations are consistent with the following mechanism.

$$N_2H_5^+ + Ox \rightarrow Red + N_2H_3 + 2H^+ \qquad \text{(slow step)}$$

The hydrazyl radical, N_2H_3, can dimerize to form tetrazane,

$$2N_2H_3 \rightarrow NH_2-NH-NH-NH_2$$

which undergoes a relatively fast reaction to form triazene and finally molecular nitrogen:

$$NH_2-NH-NH-NH_2 \rightarrow NH_3 + HN=N-NH_2$$
$$HN=N-NH_2 \rightleftharpoons NH_2-N=NH \quad \text{(rapid equilibrium)}$$
$$N_3H_3 \rightarrow NH_3 + N_2$$

Instead of dimerizing, the hydrazyl radical can be further oxidized to diimide (diazene), which undergoes rapid oxidation to N_2.

$$N_2H_3 + Ox \rightarrow Red + HN=NH + H^+$$

5-2 HYDRAZOIC ACID, HN_3

Hydrazoic acid or sodium azide, NaN_3, may be prepared in a variety of ways. (1) Sodium azide is formed when sodium nitrate is slowly added to molten sodium amide at $175°$:

$$3NaNH_2 + NaNO_3 \rightarrow NaN_3 + 3NaOH + NH_3$$

The analogous reaction with potassium salts can be carried out with somewhat higher yields in liquid ammonia at 120 to $140°$. (2) Sodium azide is formed by the reaction of nitrous oxide with molten sodium amide at $190°$:

$$2NaNH_2 + N_2O \rightarrow NaN_3 + NaOH + NH_3$$

Sodium azide is prepared commercially by carrying out the latter reaction in liquid ammonia. (3) A variety of oxidizing agents are capable of oxidizing hydrazine to hydrazoic acid. The reaction employed by Curtius, the discoverer of hydrazoic acid, was that between hydrazine and nitrous acid:

$$N_2H_5^+ + HNO_2 \rightarrow HN_3 + H^+ + 2H_2O$$

Other oxidizing agents, including hydrogen peroxide, pervanadyl ion, chlorate, peroxydisulfate, and nitric acid, give reasonable yields of hydrazoic acid.

Anhydrous hydrazoic acid is usually prepared by the dropwise addition of sulfuric acid to an alkali-metal azide. The pure acid is a fearfully explosive liquid that boils at $37°$ and freezes at $-80°$. We have already pointed out that sodium azide decomposes to the elements upon heating. The other alkali metal azides form small amounts of nitride as well as the metal and nitrogen. Azides of heavy metals such as lead, mercury, thallium, and barium explode upon sharp impact; they have been used as detonators.

Aqueous hydrazoic acid is about as strong an acid as acetic acid:

$$HN_3 = H^+ + N_3^- \qquad K = 1.8 \times 10^{-5}$$

Azides are similar in many respects to halides. Thus AgN_3 and $Hg_2(N_3)_2$ are insoluble in water. The following compounds, analogous to the interhalogens, are known: ClN_3, BrN_3, IN_3, CNN_3. Other interesting azido compounds that have been prepared are cyanuric azide, B,B,B-triazidoborazine, and the trimer of phosphonitrilic azide. The compound analogous to a halogen molecule, N_3-N_3, is unknown.

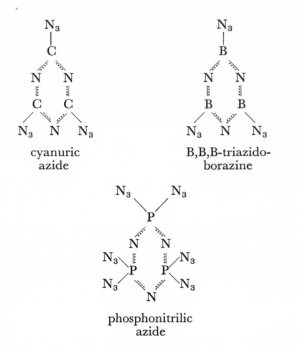

cyanuric
azide

B,B,B-triazido-
borazine

phosphonitrilic
azide

The azide ion is symmetrical and linear. The N—N bond distance (1.16 Å) is between that for a triple bond (:N≡N:, 1.098 Å) and that for a double bond (FN̈=N̈F and CH_3N̈=N̈CH_3, 1.25 Å):

$$:\ddot{N}=\overset{+}{N}=\overset{-}{\ddot{N}}: \leftrightarrow :N\equiv\overset{+}{N}-\overset{2-}{\ddot{N}}: \leftrightarrow \overset{2-}{:\ddot{N}}-\overset{+}{N}\equiv N:$$

The nitrogen nuclear magnetic resonance spectrum of a sodium azide solution consists of two peaks with intensities 2:1, indicating that there are two kinds of atoms in the azide ion—two of one kind and one of another kind. In covalent azides such as HN_3 and CH_3N_3, the azide group is still linear but asymmetrical:

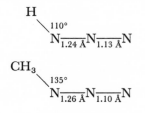

The latter compounds are resonance hybrids of the configurations

$$R—\overset{..}{\underset{..}{\overset{-}{N}}}—\overset{+}{N}{\equiv}N: \;\longleftrightarrow\; R—\overset{..}{\overset{+}{N}}{=}\overset{+}{N}{=}\overset{..}{\overset{-}{N}}:$$

5-3   MISCELLANEOUS HYDRONITROGENS

The Imide Radical, NH

When hydrazoic acid at low pressures is passed through either a heated quartz tube or an electric discharge, or is irradiated with ultraviolet light, the following reaction takes place:

$$HN_3 \rightarrow NH + N_2$$

If the reaction products impinge on a surface cooled with liquid nitrogen, a blue paramagnetic material freezes out.   It is thought to be the imide radical, NH.   When the blue material is warmed to -150 to $-125°$, the color changes to white.   Ammonium azide is formed.

Diimide, N_2H_2

Mass spectrometric examination of the products of the HN_3 electric discharge reaction indicates the presence of diimide, N_2H_2. This species probably forms via the reaction

$$NH + HN_3 \rightarrow N_2H_2 + N_2$$

Diimide is also a possible product of the photolysis of hydrazoic acid in a matrix of solid nitrogen at $20°K$.

We have already pointed out that diimide is probably an intermediate in the oxidation of aqueous hydrazine.   Diimide is believed to be the active intermediate in the hydrogenation of un-saturated linkages by mixtures of hydrazine and oxidizing agents such as oxygen–copper ion and hydrogen peroxide–copper ion:

$$HN{=}NH + X{=}Y \rightarrow N_2 + X\overset{\diagup}{\underset{H}{}}—\overset{\diagdown}{\underset{H}{}}Y$$

Solutions of azodicarboxylic acid, $HOOCN{=}NCOOH$, are reducing agents for double bonds, and it is believed that diimide (formed by a decarboxylation reaction) is the active hydrogenator:

$$HOOCN{=}NCOOH \rightarrow 2CO_2 + HN{=}NH$$

When olefins are heated with p-toluenesulfonylhydrazine, the double bonds are hydrogenated. It is believed that the latter reagent thermally decomposes to, among other things, p-toluenesulfinic acid and diimide:

$$CH_3C_6H_4SO_2NHNH_2 \rightarrow CH_3C_6H_4SO_2H + HN{=}NH$$

The Amide Radical, NH_2

The thermal decomposition of hydrazine to N_2, H_2, and NH_3 is a free-radical reaction that is in part heterogeneous. The initial step in the process is believed to be the cleavage of the N—N bond to form two amide radicals,

$$N_2H_4 \rightarrow 2NH_2$$

followed by the formation of the hydrazyl radical:

$$NH_2 + N_2H_4 \rightarrow NH_3 + N_2H_3$$

The hydrazyl radical probably decomposes on the wall as follows:

$$2N_2H_3 \rightarrow 2NH_3 + N_2$$

The activation energy for the decomposition of hydrazine is about 60 kcal/mole. If we assume that the activation energy for the recombination of two NH_2 radicals to form hydrazine is zero, we may take $D = 60$ kcal/mole for the N—N bond dissociation energy of hydrazine. This is to be compared with the bond energy $E = 38$ kcal/mole calculated from thermochemical data with the assumption that the average N—H bond energy in hydrazine is the same as the average N—H bond energy in ammonia. From these data one concludes that the NH_2—H dissociation energy is considerably greater than the average of the NH—H and N—H dissociation energies.

5-4 ORGANOSUBSTITUTED FREE RADICALS

When the colorless solution of tetraphenylhydrazine in toluene is heated, a greenish-brown color forms reversibly. The color is attributable to the diphenylamide radical.

$$(C_6H_5)_2NN(C_6H_5)_2 \rightleftharpoons 2(C_6H_5)_2N\cdot$$

The remarkable compound 1,1-diphenyl-2-picrylhydrazyl exists entirely as a free radical, both in solutions and in the solid state. A few of the structures contributing to the resonance hybrid are given below. This compound is often used for calibrating electron-spin-resonance and Gouy balance apparatuses.

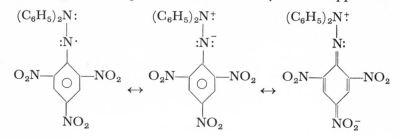

5-5 HYDROXYLAMINE, NH$_2$OH

Preparation

Hydroxylamine may be prepared in at least four different ways. One method involves the hydrolysis of primary aliphatic nitro compounds such as 1-nitropropane and 1,2-dinitroethane. The reaction is usually carried out in relatively concentrated sulfuric acid, and it may involve intermediates such as those indicated in the following scheme:

$$RCH_2NO_2 \rightarrow RCH{=}\overset{\overset{\displaystyle O}{|}}{N}{-}OH \rightarrow R\overset{\overset{\displaystyle OH}{|}}{C}{=}N{-}OH \rightarrow$$

$$RCOOH + H_2NOH$$

Since the nitro compounds are readily prepared by the vapor-phase nitration of paraffin hydrocarbons, the method is useful not only for preparing hydroxylamine but also for preparing acids such as propionic and butyric acids.

A second preparative method involves the platinum-catalyzed hydrogenation of nitric oxide in aqueous acid:

$$NO + \tfrac{3}{2}H_2 + H^+ \rightarrow NH_3OH^+$$

By using a platinum-on-carbon catalyst, a pH less than 2.25, and NO:H$_2$ ratios of 1:2 to 1:3, yields as high as 73 per cent have been obtained.

A third method for preparing hydroxylamine is the electrolytic reduction of a sulfuric or hydrochloric acid solution containing nitric acid. The current efficiency is strongly influenced by the nature of the cathode material. Yields as high as 69 per cent have been obtained with amalgamated-lead electrodes, whereas smooth-copper electrodes give yields of about 11 per cent.

A fourth preparative method, readily carried out in the laboratory, involves the reduction of nitrous acid by bisulfite. The first step involves the formation of hydroxylimidodisulfate:

$$HNO_2 + 2HSO_3^- \rightarrow HON(SO_3)_2^{2-} + H_2O$$

The $HON(SO_3)_2^{2-}$ ion is stable in alkaline solution but undergoes rapid hydrolysis to form hydroxylamidosulfate in acid solution:

$$HON(SO_3)_2^{2-} + H_2O \rightarrow HONHSO_3^- + HSO_4^-$$

The latter species is much more resistant toward hydrolysis than the disulfate. When heated in 0.5 M HCl at 100° for an hour, the hydroxylammonium ion forms:

$$H^+ + HONHSO_3^- + H_2O \rightarrow NH_3OH^+ + HSO_4^-$$

Anhydrous, free hydroxylamine may be prepared by treating a suspension of hydroxylammonium chloride in butanol with a solution of sodium butoxide:

$$NH_3OHCl + C_4H_9ONa \rightarrow NH_2OH + NaCl + C_4H_9OH$$

The sodium chloride is filtered off and the hydroxylamine is precipitated by the addition of ether and cooling.

Physical and Chemical Properties

Pure hydroxylamine is an extremely unstable compound that melts at 33° and boils at 58° under 22 mm pressure. It decomposes above 15° to ammonia, water, and a mixture of nitrogen and nitrous oxide. Aqueous solutions are much more stable, particularly acid solutions in which the molecule is protonated as NH_3OH^+. The equilibrium constant for the basic ionization of hydroxylamine is 6.6×10^{-9}.

$$NH_2OH + H_2O = NH_3OH^+ + OH^-$$

The weaker basicity of hydroxylamine compared with that of ammonia ($K_b = 1.8 \times 10^{-5}$) is not unexpected. Hydroxylamine may be looked upon as ammonia in which one of the hydrogens has been replaced by the more electron-attracting hydroxyl group.

Because of the instability of the free base, a complete structure determination has not been carried out for hydroxylamine. X-ray data yield N—O distances of 1.48 Å for free hydroxylamine and 1.45 Å for hydroxylammonium salts.

REFERENCES

G. Yagil and M. Anbar, "The kinetics of hydrazine formation from chloramine and ammonia," *J. Am. Chem. Soc.*, **84**, 1797 (1962).

L. F. Audrieth and B. A. Ogg, *The Chemistry of Hydrazine*, Wiley, New York, 1951.

"Recent aspects of the inorganic chemistry of nitrogen," *Chem. Soc.* (*London*), *Spec. Publ.* 10 (1957).

L. F. Audrieth, "Hydrazoic acid and its inorganic derivatives," *Chem. Rev.*, **15**, 169 (1934).

D. M. Yost and H. Russell, Jr., *Systematic Inorganic Chemistry*, Prentice-Hall, Englewood Cliffs, N.J., 1944.

6

Nitrogen Oxides and Oxy-acids

A wide variety of oxides, oxy-acids, and oxy-anions of nitrogen, corresponding to oxidation states of nitrogen from $+1$ to $+5$, have been characterized. The more important of these are listed in Table 6-1.

Table 6-1 *Nitrogen oxides and oxy-acids*

Formula	Name	Melting point, °C	Boiling point, °C	Remarks
N_2O	Nitrous oxide	-90.86	-88.48	Relatively unreactive
$H_2N_2O_2$	Hyponitrous acid			Unstable, weak acid
NH_2NO_2	Nitramide			Unstable, weak acid
NO	Nitric oxide	-163.65	-151.77	Moderately reactive
HNO	Nitroxyl			Unknown except as kinetic intermediate and as salts

(cont.)

Table 6-1   *Nitrogen oxides and oxy-acids (continued)*

$H_2N_2O_3$				Unstable; known in solution and as salts
H_2NO_2	Hydronitrous acid			Explosive sodium salt known
N_2O_3	Dinitrogen trioxide	-111	2	Largely dissociated to NO and NO_2
HNO_2	Nitrous acid			Unstable, but salts stable
HOONO	Pernitrous acid			Unstable, but anion stable
N_2O_4	Dinitrogen tetroxide	-11.20	21.15	Colorless; largely dissociated to brown NO_2
NO_2	Nitrogen dioxide			Brown, reactive gas
N_2O_5	Dinitrogen pentoxide	Sublimes 32.4°		Unstable vapor
HNO_3	Nitric acid	-41.60	83	Strong acid
HNO_4	Peroxynitric acid			Unstable
NO_3				Unstable intermediate

6-1   NITROUS OXIDE, N_2O

Nitrous oxide is readily obtained by the thermal decomposition of substances with the empirical formula $N_2O \cdot xH_2O$ (such as ammonium nitrate, hyponitrous acid, and nitramide). The molecule is linear with the two nitrogen atoms adjacent to one another, NNO. The N—N bond distance is 1.126 Å, between the distances expected for a triple bond (1.098 Å) and a double bond (1.25 Å). The N—O bond distance is 1.186 Å, between the distances expected for a double bond (1.15 Å) and a single bond (~ 1.4 Å). The bond distances may be explained in terms of resonance between the structures $N\!\equiv\!\overset{+}{N}\!-\!\overset{-}{O}$ and $\overset{-}{N}\!=\!\overset{+}{N}\!=\!O$.

At least two different explanations may be given for the fact that nitrous oxide does not have the structure NON. First, the latter structure involves a greater amount of electrostatic repulsion between adjacent atomic kernels than does the structure NNO. The nitrogen kernel has a charge of $+5$, and the oxygen kernel has a charge of $+6$. The repulsion between two adjacent kernels may be measured by the product of the charges. For NON we have $5 \times 6 + 5 \times 6 = 60$, whereas for NNO we have $5 \times 5 + 5 \times 6 = 55$. Second, the only satisfactory electronic structure for NON involves placing a $+2$ formal charge on the oxygen atom and -1 formal charges on the nitrogen atoms: $\overset{-}{N}\!\!=\!\!\overset{+2}{O}\!\!=\!\!\overset{-}{N}$. Not only is a $+2$ formal charge almost unknown for oxygen, but such a distribution of charge contradicts the fact that oxygen is more electronegative than nitrogen.

Compared to the other nitrogen oxides, nitrous oxide is relatively inert. It reacts only slowly with oxidizing and reducing agents. Nitrous oxide decomposes into its elements at an appreciable rate when heated above 600°. This process is unimolecular and has an activation energy of 59 kcal/mole. From a consideration of the energetics of the following elementary processes,

$$N_2O \rightarrow N_2 + O(^3P) \qquad \Delta H° = 39.7 \text{ kcal/mole}$$
$$N_2O \rightarrow N_2 + O(^1D) \qquad \Delta H° = 85.1 \text{ kcal/mole}$$
$$N_2O \rightarrow N + NO \qquad \Delta H° = 115.1 \text{ kcal/mole}$$

it is clear that the first of these processes is the rate-determining step of the decomposition. It is noteworthy that in this process there is a change in the total electron spin. Although the spin conservation rule (which requires zero change in total electron spin in elementary processes) is seldom violated in spectroscopy, it is possible that it is more commonly violated in kinetics.

The extrapolated entropy of N_2O at 0°K is not zero, as it should be for a perfectly ordered crystal, but rather 1.14 eu. This value is close to $R \ln 2 = 1.38$, predicted for a structure with N_2O molecules randomly placed in one or the other of two possible positions, NNO and ONN. X-ray and neutron-diffraction studies are consistent with such a disordered structure.

6-2 HYPONITROUS ACID, $H_2N_2O_2$

Hyponitrous acid is a dibasic acid with the structure HON=NOH. The ionization constants are $K_1 = 9 \times 10^{-8}$ and $K_2 = 1 \times 10^{-11}$. In solid salts, the hyponitrite ion has the trans configuration indicated on page 72.

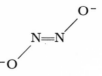

White crystals of hyponitrous acid may be obtained by evaporating the solution prepared by treating the silver salt with ethereal hydrogen chloride.

$$Ag_2N_2O_2 + 2HCl \rightarrow 2AgCl + H_2N_2O_2$$

The solid decomposes to nitrogen, nitrogen oxides, and water. Aqueous solutions decompose principally to nitrous oxide and water. The main rate-determining step is the decomposition of the $HN_2O_2^-$ ion,

$$HN_2O_2^- \rightarrow N_2O + OH^-$$

but other processes are involved, including a free-radical chain reaction initiated by the step $HON{=}NOH \rightarrow N_2 + 2OH$. Generally, the hydroxyl radicals react with $H_2N_2O_2$ to form nitrate.

Hyponitrites may be prepared in a variety of ways, including the reduction of nitrite by sodium amalgam:

$$2NO_2^- + 4Na + 2H_2O \rightarrow N_2O_2^{2-} + 4Na^+ + 4OH^-$$

6-3 NITRAMIDE, NH_2NO_2

A common starting material for the preparation of nitramide is ethyl carbamate. This reacts with ethyl nitrate in concentrated sulfuric acid to form ethyl nitrocarbamate. The latter compound is saponified to the potassium salt which, when treated with cold dilute acid, yields nitramide. The nitramide may be isolated by extraction with ether.

$$C_2H_5OCONH_2 + C_2H_5ONO_2 \rightarrow$$
$$C_2H_5OCONHNO_2 + C_2H_5OH$$
$$C_2H_5OCONHNO_2 + 2KOH \rightarrow$$
$$K_2(OCONNO_2) + C_2H_5OH + H_2O$$
$$K_2(OCONNO_2) + 2H^+ \rightarrow NH_2NO_2 + CO_2 + 2K^+$$

Nitramide is a weak acid in aqueous solution:

$$NH_2NO_2 = H^+ + NHNO_2^- \qquad K = 2.6 \times 10^{-7}$$

As is the case with the isomeric hyponitrous acid, nitramide decomposes to nitrous oxide and water in aqueous solution. The decomposition is an example of a general base-catalyzed reaction.

$$NH_2NO_2 + B \xrightarrow{slow} NHNO_2^- + BH^+$$

$$NHNO_2^- \xrightarrow{fast} N_2O + OH^-$$

For a number of bases in solution, each contributes to the rate according to the expression

$$\frac{d[N_2O]}{dt} = [NH_2NO_2] \sum_i k_i[B_i]$$

6-4 NITRIC OXIDE, NO

Nitric oxide is manufactured by the atmospheric oxidation of ammonia on platinum gauze or other catalysts at temperatures of about 500°.

$$4NH_3 + 5O_2 \rightarrow 4NO + 6H_2O$$

In the absence of the catalyst, nitrogen is one of the main products of the oxidation of ammonia. In the laboratory, nitric oxide may be prepared from aqueous solution by the reaction of nitrous acid and iodide

$$2HNO_2 + 2I^- + 2H^+ \rightarrow 2NO + I_2 + 2H_2O$$

Although gaseous NO is essentially colorless, in the liquid and solid states NO is blue.

According to simple molecular orbital theory, nitric oxide has the electronic configuration $KK(s\sigma)^2(s\sigma^*)^2(p\pi)^4(p\sigma)^2(p\pi^*)$, corresponding to a bond order of $2\frac{1}{2}$. Nitric oxide has one more electron than molecular nitrogen has, but since the additional electron is in an antibonding orbital, the bond order is less than that in N_2 by one-half unit. The same conclusion may be reached by using Linnett's modification of the Lewis octet theory. If we divide the eleven valence electrons into a group of six with the same spin ($\overset{\times}{\underset{\times}{\text{N}}}\overset{\times}{\text{O}}\overset{\times}{}$) and a group of five with the opposite spin ($\circ\overset{\circ}{\underset{\circ}{\text{N}}}\overset{\circ}{\text{O}}\circ$), we have the resultant structure $\overset{\times}{}\text{N}\overset{\times}{=\!\!=}\overset{\circ}{\text{O}}\overset{\times}{}$. This structure indicates the existence of one unpaired electron and a bond order of $2\frac{1}{2}$.

It is remarkable that an odd molecule (a molecule possessing an odd number of electrons) like NO shows practically no evidence of dimerization in the gaseous state. However, the very high entropy of vaporization at the boiling point (27.13 eu) indicates that some association takes place in the liquid. And the solid consists of loose dimers which are believed to have the structure shown below.

$$N \text{ —— —— —— ——} O$$
$$| \qquad\qquad\qquad | \; 1.10 \text{ Å}$$
$$O \text{ —— —— —— ——} N$$
$$2.38 \text{ Å}$$

Most free radicals dimerize because there is an increase in the total number of bonds upon dimerization. It will be noted that no such increase accompanies the dimerization of 2NO to O=N—N=O.

Nitric oxide reacts rapidly with oxygen to form brown NO_2.

$$2NO + O_2 \rightarrow 2NO_2$$

For this reason, it is often mistakenly concluded that NO_2 is formed in reactions that are carried out in open vessels and that actually involve the initial evolution of only NO. The reaction follows a simple third-order rate law

$$\frac{-d[NO]}{dt} = k[NO]^2[O_2]$$

and the reaction was first interpreted as being termolecular. However, the rate constant is very unusual in having a negative

Table 6-2 Rate constants for the reaction $2NO + O_2 \rightarrow 2NO_2$

T, °K	$k \times 10^{-9}$, $cm^6 \, mole^{-2} \, sec^{-1}$
273.1	7.88
333.2	5.58
470.0	3.34
563.6	2.82
661.9	2.54

temperature coefficient (see Table 6-2). Thus a more plausible mechanism is one involving the equilibrium

$$2NO = N_2O_2$$

preceding the bimolecular rate-determining step

$$N_2O_2 + O_2 \xrightarrow{k'} 2NO_2$$

This leads to the rate law

$$\frac{-d[NO]}{dt} = k'K[NO]^2[O_2]$$

where K is the equilibrium constant for the preliminary equilibrium and $k = k'K$. Since K should decrease with increasing temperature, it is quite reasonable for $k'K$ also to do so.

　　Nitric oxide is like carbon monoxide in forming complexes with transition metals. The extra antibonding electron of NO is usually transferred to the metal atom to give the nitrosyl cation, $N{\equiv}O^+$. Typical complexes are $Fe(CN)_6NO^{2-}$ and $FeNO(H_2O)_5^{2+}$. In some complexes, such as $Co(NH_3)_5NO^{2+}$, an electron is transferred from the metal to NO to form $O{=}N^-$.

　　When highly purified hydrogen chloride is rapidly condensed with liquid nitrogen, the solid is red. It is thought that traces of nitric oxide cause this color, inasmuch as purposeful addition of 10^{-4} or 10^{-5} mole fraction of nitric oxide intensifies the color. It is possible that the color is due to a compound $NO \cdot HCl$, comparable to the red $NO \cdot BF_3$ that is formed from NO and BF_3.

6-5 THE NITROSYL CATION, NO$^+$

　　The ionization potential of nitric oxide (9.25 eV) is lower than that of similar molecules (N_2, 15.58; O_2, 12.2); the increase in bond strength accompanying ionization is evidenced by the stretching frequency of 2200 cm^{-1} for NO$^+$ as compared with 1840 cm^{-1} for NO.

　　The nitrosyl ion is formed when either N_2O_3 or N_2O_4 is dissolved in concentrated sulfuric acid:

$$N_2O_3 + 3H_2SO_4 = 2NO^+ + 3HSO_4^- + H_3O^+$$

$$N_2O_4 + 3H_2SO_4 = NO^+ + NO_2^+ + 3HSO_4^- + H_3O^+$$

The salt $NOHSO_4$ (nitrosyl bisulfate) may be isolated from the solutions. Liquid nitrosyl chloride is believed to ionize to NO$^+$

and Cl⁻. Many metal chlorides form NOCl addition compounds that are nitrosyl salts and that dissolve in nitrosyl chloride to form conducting solutions. Examples are $(NO)_2TiCl_6$, $NO(AuCl_4)$, and $NO(AlCl_4)$.

6-6 SOME UNUSUAL OXY-ACIDS AND OXY-ANIONS OF NITROGEN

Nitroxyl, HNO

It is often assumed that two-electron reducing agents such as stannous ion react with nitrous acid to form an unstable intermediate called nitroxyl, HNO. This species may either decompose to nitrous oxide or be further reduced to hydroxylamine. Similarly, nitroxyl may be formed by the oxidation of hydroxylamine by oxidizing agents such as ferric ion. Nitroxyl has been formed by the photolysis of methyl nitrite in a matrix of solid argon at 20°K:

$$CH_3ONO + h\nu \rightarrow CH_2O + HNO$$

Infrared spectra suggest the structure H—N=O, with an H—N—O angle of approximately 110°.

Liquid ammonia solutions of sodium, potassium, and barium react with nitric oxide to form white precipitates of NaNO, KNO, and $Ba(NO)_2$. The NaNO compound has an X-ray pattern different from that of ordinary sodium *trans*-hyponitrite, and it may actually be sodium *cis*-hyponitrite.

The Trioxodinitrate(II) Ion, $N_2O_3^{2-}$

The sodium salt of this anion may be prepared by the reaction of ethyl nitrate with an alcoholic solution of hydroxylamine and sodium ethoxide:

$$2NaOEt + EtONO_2 + NH_2OH \rightarrow Na_2N_2O_3 + 3EtOH$$

The anion is believed to have the structure shown below.

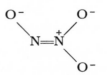

Aqueous solutions of the sodium salt are reasonably stable; the alkaline earth, lead, and cadmium salts may be precipitated by metathesis.   Addition of acid causes immediate decomposition to nitric oxide and water.

$$H_2N_2O_3 \rightarrow 2NO + H_2O$$

The Hydronitrite Ion, NO_2^{2-}

When a liquid ammonia solution of sodium nitrite is electrolyzed, or when a sodium-ammonia solution is treated with sodium nitrite, a highly explosive yellow precipitate of empirical formula Na_2NO_2 is formed.   The material is only weakly paramagnetic, suggesting that the compound is largely dimerized as $Na_4N_2O_4$.

6-7 DINITROGEN TRIOXIDE, N_2O_3

When an equimolar mixture of NO and NO_2 is condensed, a blue liquid that freezes at $-111°$ to a blue solid is formed.   Spectroscopic data are consistent with the following structure for N_2O_3:

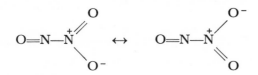

The following bond distances have been estimated from infrared data: nitroso bond, 1.12 Å; nitro bond, 1.18 Å; and N—N bond, 2.08 Å.

The gaseous equilibrium

$$N_2O_3 = NO + NO_2$$

has equilibrium constants (extrapolated to $P = 0$) of 2.10, 3.67, and 6.88 atm at 25°, 35°, and 45°, respectively.

Dinitrogen trioxide may be looked upon as the anhydride of nitrous acid.   It reacts with alkaline solutions to give practically pure nitrite:

$$N_2O_3 + 2OH^- \rightarrow 2NO_2^- + H_2O$$

When N_2O_3 reacts with water, appreciable amounts of NO, N_2O_4, and nitrate are formed in addition to nitrous acid.

6-8 NITROUS ACID AND NITRITES, HNO$_2$ AND NO$_2^-$

In the gaseous state, N_2O_3 (in equilibrium with NO and NO_2) reacts with water to form nitrous acid vapor. The reaction may be represented as follows:

$$NO(g) + NO_2(g) + H_2O(g) = 2HNO_2(g)$$

At 25°, the equilibrium constant for the reaction is 1.27 atm^{-1}.

Aqueous solutions of nitrous acid may be prepared by the addition of a strong acid to a solution of a nitrite. Nitrous acid is a weak acid with an ionization constant of 4.5×10^{-4}. Solutions of the acid decompose reversibly and at a measurable rate to give nitric oxide and nitrate:

$$3HNO_2 = H^+ + NO_3^- + 2NO + H_2O$$

The rate of the forward reaction is given by the expression

$$-\frac{d[HNO_2]}{dt} = \frac{k_1[HNO_2]^4}{P_{NO}^2}$$

and the rate of the reverse reaction by the expression

$$\frac{d[HNO_2]}{dt} = k_2[HNO_2][H^+][NO_3^-]$$

where, at 25°, $k_1 = 46$ and $k_2 = 1.6$ for concentrations in molarity, pressures in atmospheres, and time in minutes. The decomposition is believed to proceed by the following mechanism.

$$4HNO_2 = N_2O_4 + 2NO + 2H_2O \qquad \text{(rapid, reversible)}$$
$$N_2O_4 \to NO^+ + NO_3^- \qquad \text{(rate-determining)}$$
$$NO^+ + H_2O = HNO_2 + H^+ \qquad \text{(rapid, reversible)}$$

Secondary amines react with nitrous acid to form stable N-nitrosoamines:

$$R_2NH + HNO_2 \to R_2NN{=}O + H_2O$$

Ammonia and primary amines are believed to form N-nitroso-amines, but the latter compounds are very unstable. The over-all reactions involve formation of nitrogen gas, in the case of ammonia and aliphatic primary amines, and formation of diazonium salts, in the case of aromatic primary amines.

$$NH_3 + HNO_2 \to N_2 + 2H_2O$$
$$RNH_2 + HNO_2 \to N_2 + ROH + H_2O$$
$$ArNH_3^+ + HNO_2 \to ArN_2^+ + 2H_2O$$

These nitrosation reactions proceed by a variety of mechanisms; the mechanism in each case depends on the concentrations of reagents and on the nature of the amine.   At low concentrations of nitrous acid, the rate is usually expressible by the equation, rate = k[amine][HNO_2][H^+].   The nitrosyl ion, NO^+, or its hydrated equivalent, the nitrous acidium ion, $H_2NO_2^+$, is believed to be formed in an initial rapid equilibrium:

$$H^+ + HNO_2 \rightleftharpoons NO^+ + H_2O \qquad K = 2 \times 10^{-7} \ (20°)$$

The nitrosyl ion then reacts with the amine in a rate-determining step:

$$NO^+ + amine \rightarrow nitrosoamine + H^+$$

At higher concentrations of nitrous acid and at high acidities, the rate equation is rate = k[amine][HNO_2]^2.   Under these conditions the nitrosating reagent is N_2O_3:

$$2HNO_2 \rightarrow H_2O + N_2O_3 \qquad \text{(rapid)}$$
$$amine + N_2O_3 \rightarrow nitrosoamine + HNO_2 \qquad \text{(slow)}$$

At low acidities, there is plenty of free amine to react with the N_2O_3 as the latter is formed, and the slow step is the production of N_2O_3 from two molecules of HNO_2.   Thus the rate equation becomes rate = k[HNO_2]^2.

Nitrites may be prepared either by thermal decomposition of alkali nitrates,

$$2KNO_3 \rightarrow 2KNO_2 + O_2$$

or by reduction of nitrates by carbon or lead.

$$2KNO_3 + C \rightarrow 2KNO_2 + CO_2$$

The lone pair of electrons in the nitrite ion is sterically significant; consequently, the nitrite ion is bent:

The N—O bond distance has been reported as 1.24 Å with a bond angle of 115°.

6-9 PEROXYNITROUS ACID, HOONO

Nitrous acid reacts with hydrogen peroxide to give nitrate:

$$H_2O_2 + HNO_2 \rightarrow NO_3^- + H_2O + H^+$$

The rate of the reaction may be represented by the following expression:

$$-\frac{d[H_2O_2]}{dt} = \frac{k_1[H^+][HNO_2][H_2O_2]}{1 + k_2[H_2O_2]}$$

At low concentrations of hydrogen peroxide, the rate is first order in hydrogen peroxide; at very high concentrations of hydrogen peroxide, the rate is independent of that reagent. The following mechanism is consistent with these facts:

$$HNO_2 + H^+ \rightleftharpoons NO^+ + H_2O$$
$$H_2O_2 + NO^+ \rightarrow HOONO + H^+$$
$$HOONO + H^+ \rightarrow 2H^+ + NO_3^-$$

The intermediate peroxynitrous acid, HOONO, is unstable in acid solution, but the peroxynitrite ion is stable. Thus, if a solution of nitrous acid and peroxide is made alkaline soon after mixing, as much as 70 per cent of the nitrite appears as peroxynitrite.

It is believed that peroxynitrous acid decomposes to some extent to OH and NO_2 radicals, since a mixture of hydrogen peroxide and nitrous acid brings about the polymerization of methyl methacrylate and the hydroxylation and nitration of benzene.

6-10 DINITROGEN TETROXIDE AND NITROGEN DIOXIDE; N_2O_4 AND NO_2

In gaseous and liquid states, these oxides always exist in the presence of one another. The reaction

$$2NO_2(g) = N_2O_4(g)$$

rapidly achieves equilibrium; at 25°, $K = 8.8$ atm^{-1}. In the solid state, the material exists as pure N_2O_4. Nitrogen dioxide is brown and paramagnetic; dinitrogen tetroxide is colorless and diamagnetic.

Nitrogen dioxide has a V-shaped structure; the N—O bond distance is 1.19 Å, and the bond angle is 134°. Although the bonding may be described in terms of molecular orbital theory, the following Linnett-type structures maintain an octet of electrons around each atom:

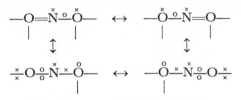

Dinitrogen tetroxide has a remarkable structure:

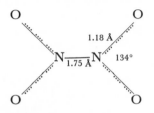

The N—N bond is much longer than an ordinary N—N single bond (the N—N distance is 1.47 Å in hydrazine). This, together with the fact that the O—N—O bond angles in NO_2 and N_2O_4 are the same, suggests that N_2O_4 corresponds to a pair of NO_2 molecules very loosely held together. However, the N_2O_4 molecule is planar, and there is no obvious reason why there should not be free rotation of the NO_2 groups about the N—N bond. Low-temperature infrared studies indicate the existence of two other forms of N_2O_4: a form in which the two NO_2 groups are in planes that are at right angles to each other and a form with the structure O=N—O—NO_2.

The chemistry of liquid N_2O_4 suggests that in the pure liquid (as well as in solvents such as sulfuric acid and dimethyl sulfoxide), N_2O_4 self-ionizes:

$$N_2O_4 = NO^+ + NO_3^-$$

According to the solvent system of acids and bases, the nitrosyl ion should be the acidic species in N_2O_4 and the nitrate ion should be the basic species. Thus one may look upon the reaction of NOCl in N_2O_4 with silver nitrate as a neutralization reaction:

$$NOCl + AgNO_3(s) \rightarrow AgCl(s) + N_2O_4$$

Alkali metals react with liquid N_2O_4 to release nitric oxide:

$$M + N_2O_4 \rightarrow NO + MNO_3$$

Metals such as zinc, iron, and tin react with nitrosyl chloride in liquid N_2O_4 as follows:

$$M + 2NOCl \rightarrow MCl_2 + 2NO$$

Copper metal reacts with a solution of N_2O_4 in ethyl acetate to yield crystalline $Cu(NO_3)_2 \cdot N_2O_4$, which may be better represented as $NO[Cu(NO_3)_3]$. When the latter compound is heated, N_2O_4 is lost, and anhydrous, volatile (at 150 to 200°) $Cu(NO_3)_2$ is obtained.

Dinitrogen tetroxide forms a wide variety of addition compounds with oxygen and nitrogen bases. Strong bases such as R_3N form ionic compounds that probably have structures such as $(R_3N-N{=}O)^+(NO_3)^-$. Weaker bases such as ethers, carbonyl compounds, and sulfoxides form addition compounds in which the N_2O_4 molecule remains intact. Thus 1,4-dioxane forms a very stable 1:1 compound whose crystal structure consists of infinite chains of alternating $C_4H_8O_2$ and N_2O_4 molecules. The N_2O_4 molecules are planar and perpendicular to the axis of the chain. The structure is pictured in Figure 6-1.

Dinitrogen tetroxide reacts with boron trifluoride to form $N_2O_4 \cdot 2BF_3$, which has the remarkable structure

$$NO_2^+ (F_3BO-N-OBF_3)^-$$

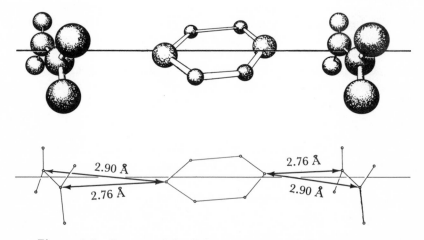

Figure 6-1 Structure of the dinitrogen tetroxide 1,4-dioxane complex. The crystal consists of chains of alternating N_2O_4 and $C_4H_8O_2$ molecules.

6-11   DINITROGEN PENTOXIDE, N$_2$O$_5$

Dinitrogen pentoxide is a colorless volatile solid which may be made in either of two ways.   In the first way, nitric acid is dehydrated with phosphorus(V) oxide and the N$_2$O$_5$ is distilled in a current of ozone and oxygen.

$$2HNO_3 + P_2O_5 \rightarrow \frac{2}{x}(HPO_3)_x + N_2O_5$$

In the second way, N$_2$O$_4$ is treated directly with ozone:

$$N_2O_4 + O_3 \rightarrow N_2O_5 + O_2$$

Since N$_2$O$_5$ is the anhydride of nitric acid, it is deliquescent and reacts with water as follows:

$$N_2O_5 + H_2O \rightarrow 2HNO_3$$

The gaseous molecule probably has the structure O$_2$N—O—NO$_2$, but the solid consists of an ionic lattice of nitryl ions, NO$_2^+$, and nitrate ions, NO$_3^-$.

6-12   NITRIC ACID, HNO$_3$

Nitric acid is generally made by the absorption in water of NO$_2$ obtained from the oxidation of ammonia.

$$3NO_2(g) + H_2O = 2H^+ + 2NO_3^- + NO(g)$$

The reaction with water is rapid initially, but as the concentration of nitric acid builds up, it becomes very slow, largely because the equilibrium pressure of nitric oxide becomes very small.   Therefore, in order to prepare acid of concentration greater than 50 per cent, a mixture of NO$_2$ and oxygen is passed into water, the oxygen serving to oxidize the NO formed in the reaction.   The 68.4 per cent acid is a constant-boiling mixture with a boiling point of 122°.   Therefore, 100 per cent nitric acid is prepared by distillation of a mixture of aqueous nitric acid and fuming sulfuric acid.

The phase diagram of the H$_2$O–HNO$_3$ system (see Figure 6-1) indicates the existence of two hydrates of nitric acid: a monohydrate that melts at $-37.7°$ and a trihydrate that melts at $-18.5°$. In dilute aqueous solutions nitric acid is a completely strong acid; that is, it is completely ionized.   However, Raman spectra of nitric acid solutions indicate that ionization is incomplete at concentrations as low as 3 M and that at higher concentrations a large fraction of the acid is in the form of HNO_3 molecules. The Raman-determined value for the ionization constant of nitric acid is $K = 21$. In nonaqueous solvents of low dielectric constant, such as acetic acid, nitric acid has been shown to be a much weaker acid than other "strong" acids like $HClO_4$, HBr, H_2SO_4, and HCl.

Nitric acid is an oxidizing agent, but both the rate of its reactions and its reduction products are strongly influenced by concentration. Thus in solutions that are less than 1 M in concentration, iodine is formed very slowly from iodide solutions; whereas at concentrations greater than 2 M, iodine, bromine, and even chlorine are rapidly liberated from halide salts. At low concentrations the principal reduction product of nitric acid is NO, whereas at higher concentrations considerable amounts of NO_2 are evolved. The metals gold, platinum, rhodium, and iridium are not attacked by hot concentrated nitric acid. But these metals may be dissolved by aqua regia, which is a mixture of three parts of concentrated HCl to one part of concentrated HNO_3. The effectiveness of aqua regia is due in part to the presence of both chlorine and nitrosyl chloride,

$$4H^+ + NO_3^- + 3Cl^- = NOCl + Cl_2 + 2H_2O$$

and in part to the complexing ability of the chloride ion, which forms species such as $AuCl_4^-$ with the dissolved metal ions.

The structure of the gaseous HNO_3 molecule is shown below.

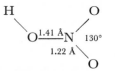

The nitrogen atom and oxygen atoms are coplanar.

The nitrate ion is planar, the three oxygens occupying the corners of an equilateral triangle. The NO bond distance is 1.22 Å. The ion may be considered a resonance hybrid of three structures:

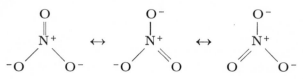

6-13 PEROXYNITRIC ACID, HNO_4

The very unstable compound HNO_4 may be prepared by the reaction of 100 per cent H_2O_2 with an excess of pure N_2O_5 at $-80°$. The pure compound decomposes explosively at $-30°$. A 70 per cent aqueous solution is fairly stable; more dilute solutions hydrolyze rapidly.

6-14 NITROGEN TRIOXIDE, NO_3

Dinitrogen pentoxide readily decomposes to give dinitrogen tetroxide and oxygen,

$$2N_2O_5 = 2N_2O_4 + O_2$$

This reaction was the first homogeneous first-order reaction in the gas phase to be reported. It has been shown, however, that in spite of being first order the reaction is not unimolecular and has a complex mechanism. Ogg has pointed out that the data may be explained by the following mechanism:

$$N_2O_5 = NO_2 + NO_3$$
$$NO_2 + NO_3 \rightarrow NO_2 + O_2 + NO$$
$$NO + NO_3 \rightarrow 2NO_2$$

Thus the reaction involves a preliminary equilibrium followed by a bimolecular rate-determining step. The last reaction (between NO and NO_3 to form $2NO_2$) proceeds essentially to completion, but the reverse reaction is sometimes important. An example of the reverse reaction is found in the reaction of NO_2 with methane to form nitromethane. The rate-determining step is the bimolecular reaction to form NO and NO_3 followed by

$$NO_3 + CH_4 \rightarrow HNO_3 + CH_3$$

and

$$CH_3 + NO_2 \rightarrow CH_3NO_2$$

The molecule NO_3 is believed to be formed when ozone reacts with nitrogen dioxide:

$$NO_2 + O_3 \rightarrow NO_3 + O_2$$
$$NO_2 + NO_3 \rightarrow N_2O_5$$

The NO_3 radical discussed in the preceding paragraphs is believed to have a symmetrical structure similar to that of the nitrate ion. An isomeric form of NO_3, presumably with the structure OONO, has been detected as a transient species in the reaction of oxygen with nitric oxide at low pressure:

$$O_2 + NO \rightleftharpoons OONO$$

6-15 STRUCTURAL CORRELATIONS

The structures of the various nitrogen-oxygen compounds discussed in this chapter need not be considered as separate, unrelated examples. Many structural features may be correlated with parameters such as bond order and electronegativity. Thus the bond angles in nitrite, nitrogen dioxide, and the nitryl ion may be correlated with the number of electrons. The bond angles are $115°$ in NO_2^-, $134°$ in NO_2, and $180°$ in NO_2^+. It is obvious that as the number of nonbonding electrons increases, the bond angle decreases. If the monomeric hydronitrite ion (NO_2^{2-}) actually

Table 6-3 *Nitrogen-oxygen bond distances*

Compound	Formal bond order	Bond distance, Å
OṄ—OH, $H_2\ddot{N}$—OH	1	1.46
O_2N—OH	1	1.41
$(CH_3)_3\overset{+}{N}$—O^-	1	~1.4
$NO_3^- \begin{cases} N_2O_5 \\ NaNO_3 \end{cases}$	1.33 / 1.33	1.24 / 1.21
NO_2^-	1.5	1.24
$ClNO_2$	1.5	1.24
CH_3NO_2	1.5	1.22
$HONO_2$ (nitro group)	1.5	1.22
$N\equiv\overset{+}{N}$—$\overset{-}{O} \leftrightarrow \overset{-}{N}=\overset{+}{N}=O$	~1.5	1.19
NO_2	1.75	1.19
$ClN{=}O$	2	1.14
NO_2^+	2	1.15
NO	2.5	1.15
NO^+	3	1.06

Table 6-4 *Effect of electronegative groups on the asymmetric stretching frequency of the nitro group*

Molecule	Asym. stretch freq., cm^{-1}	Molecule	Asym. stretch freq., cm^{-1}
NO_2^+	2375	Cl_3CNO_2	1610
FNO_2	1793	Br_3CNO_2	1592
$O_2N\!\!-\!\!NO_2$	1735	R_3CNO_2	1540
$ClNO_2$	1685	$O\!\!-\!\!NO_2^-$	1375
F_3CNO_2	1625	NO_2^-	1270

exists, it will be interesting to compare its bond angle with that of the nitrite ion.

The nitrogen-oxygen bond distances in some important compounds are given in Table 6-3. It will be noted that the bond distances decrease fairly regularly with increasing bond order.

The asymmetric stretching frequency of the nitro group in compounds of the type $R\!\!-\!\!NO_2$ varies in a regular way with the electronegativity of the R group. (Perhaps it would be more accurate to say that a scale of electronegativity may be established using these stretching frequencies.) In Table 6-4, the asymmetric stretching frequencies of a number of nitro compounds are tabulated. It will be noted that the frequency of the NO_2^+ ion (essentially an NO_2 group attached to an infinitely electronegative group) is the highest in the table and that the frequency of the NO_2^- ion (an NO_2 group attached to a group of zero electronegativity) is the lowest in the table. One explanation of the trend is that an increase in the electronegativity of R causes the nitrogen atom to divert more s character to the N—O bonds, thus strengthening those bonds. Note that in NO_2^+ the σ bonds are pure sp hybrids, whereas in NO_2^- the σ bonds are hybridized somewhere between sp^2 and pure p.

REFERENCES

"Selected values of chemical thermodynamic constants," *Natl. Bur. Standards Circ.* 500, 1952.

I. C. Hisatsune, "Thermodynamic properties of some oxides of nitrogen," *J. Phys. Chem.*, **65**, 2249 (1961).

J. W. Linnett, "A modification of the Lewis-Langmuir octet rule," *J. Am. Chem. Soc.*, **83**, 2643 (1961).

D. M. Yost and H. Russell, Jr., *Systematic Inorganic Chemistry*, Prentice-Hall, Englewood Cliffs, N.J., 1946.

W. M. Latimer, *Oxidation Potentials*, 2d ed., pp. 94–96 (Discussion of nitroxyl), Prentice-Hall, Englewood Cliffs, N.J., 1952.

"Recent aspects of the inorganic chemistry of nitrogen," *Chem. Soc. (London)*, *Spec. Publ.* 10 (1957).

C. K. Ingold, *Substitution at Elements Other Than Carbon*, Chap. 2 (Electrophilic substitution at nitrogen and oxygen, illustrated by nitration and nitrosation), Weizmann Science Press, Jerusalem, 1959.

T. A. Turney and G. A. Wright, "Nitrous acid and nitrosation," *Chem. Rev.*, **59**, 497 (1959).

"Tables of interatomic distances and configuration in molecules and ions," *Chem. Soc. (London)*, *Spec. Publ.* 11 (1958).

7

Sulfur-Nitrogen Compounds

7-1 SULFUR NITRIDES

The sulfur nitrides bear practically no relationship to the oxides of nitrogen. For only one sulfur nitride, S_4N_2, is there a corresponding nitrogen oxide with the analogous formula—and even in this case the compounds probably have different structures.

The best-known and most important sulfur nitride is S_4N_4. The compound is generally made by the ammonolysis of S_2Cl_2 or SCl_2 in an inert solvent like carbon tetrachloride:

$$6S_2Cl_2 + 16NH_3 \rightarrow S_4N_4 + 8S + 12NH_4Cl$$

$$6SCl_2 + 16NH_3 \rightarrow S_4N_4 + 2S + 12NH_4Cl$$

S_4N_4 is a bright orange solid (mp 187°) that is insoluble in water but is soluble in many organic solvents. The heat of formation is +128.8 kcal/mole; the compound decomposes explosively to the elements when shocked, as by a hammer blow.

X-ray diffraction of the crystal indicates that the S_4N_4 molecule has the structure indicated in Figure 7-1. The following

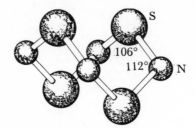

Figure 7-1 *The structure of the S_4N_4 molecule.*

classical structural formula may be written for S_4N_4, but of course the molecule is a resonance hybrid of many such structures, and there are probably contributions from structures in which the sulfur atoms utilize d orbitals:

The compounds S_7NH and $S_6(NH)_2$ are important by-products of the S_4N_4 synthesis. These molecules may be looked upon as S_8 rings in which one or two of the sulfur atoms have been replaced by —NH— groups:

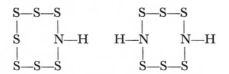

When S_7NH is treated with S_2Cl_2 or SCl_2, the compounds $S_{16}N_2$ or $S_{15}N_2$, respectively, form:

$$S_7NH + Cl—S—Cl + HNS_7 \rightarrow S_7N—S—S—NS_7 + 2HCl$$

$$S_7NH + Cl—S—Cl + HNS_7 \rightarrow S_7N—S—NS_7$$

S_4N_4 may be reduced with stannous chloride to tetrasulfur tetraimide, $S_4N_4H_4$, which has the structure shown in Figure 7-2.

When S_4N_4 is sublimed at low pressures through a tube containing silver wool at 300°, the compound S_2N_2 is formed. S_2N_2 is

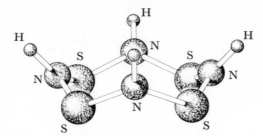

Figure 7-2   *The structure of the $S_4N_4H_4$ molecule.*

a colorless volatile solid that, on standing at room temperature, polymerizes to a blue-black material of composition $(SN)_x$. Polymeric sulfur nitride has an appreciable electrical conductivity that increases with increasing temperature.

When S_4N_4 is heated with sulfur, tetrasulfur dinitride, S_4N_2, forms. S_4N_2 is a dark red, diamagnetic, volatile material that melts at 23°. The structure is not known, but it has been suggested that the molecule is a resonating six-membered ring as follows:

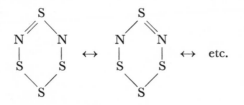

Tetrasulfur dinitride may be prepared by another method, which is quite round-about although fascinating. $S_4N_4H_4$ and mercuric acetate react in organic solvents to give the compound $Hg_5(SN)_8$. The latter compound reacts with S_2Cl_2 in carbon disulfide to give $HgCl_2$, Hg_2Cl_2, and S_4N_2.

7-2   SULFUR-NITROGEN-OXYGEN COMPOUNDS

The compound S_3N_2O may be prepared by a method analogous to the above-described method for preparing S_4N_2 from $Hg_5(SN)_8$. S_3N_2O is formed by the reaction of $Hg_5(SN)_8$ with

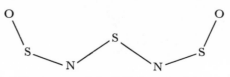

Figure 7-3   The structure of the $S_3N_2O_2$ molecule.

thionyl chloride, $SOCl_2$. S_3N_2O is a very unstable red liquid that decomposes to, among other things, S_4N_4.

The compound $S_3N_2O_2$ may be prepared by the reaction of S_4N_4 with $SOCl_2$, for which reaction the following equation has been proposed:

$$S_4N_4 + 2SOCl_2 \rightarrow S_3N_2O_2 + S_2N_2 + 2Cl_2 + S$$

A more convenient preparative method involves passing a stream of $SOCl_2$ vapor over a hot mixture of sulfur and ammonium chloride:

$$S + 6SOCl_2 + 4NH_4Cl \rightarrow 2S_3N_2O_2 + 16HCl + SO_2$$

$S_3N_2O_2$ is a yellow solid that melts at $100.7°$. The material is quite stable in the absence of moisture, but traces of moisture cause it to decompose as follows:

$$2S_3N_2O_2 \rightarrow S_4N_4 + 2SO_2$$

The structure of the $S_3N_2O_2$ molecule is presented in Figure 7-3.

$S_3N_2O_5$, a colorless volatile solid, may be prepared by the action of SO_3 on either $S_3N_2O_2$ or S_4N_4

$$S_3N_2O_2 + 3SO_3 \rightarrow S_3N_2O_5 + 3SO_2$$

$$S_4N_4 + 6SO_3 \rightarrow 2S_3N_2O_5 + 4SO_2$$

The compound is very readily hydrolyzed to sulfur dioxide, sulfate, amidosulfate, and sulfamide.

7-3 SULFUR-NITROGEN-HALOGEN COMPOUNDS

S_4N_4 and S_2Cl_2 react in the cold, either without solvent or in nitromethane, to form a green crystalline compound of empirical formula S_3N_2Cl:

$$S_4N_4 + S_2Cl_2 \rightarrow 2S_3N_2Cl$$

The material is insoluble in organic solvents and is rapidly hydrolyzed by water; so its molecular weight is unknown.

When S_3N_2Cl is heated in an indifferent solvent like carbon tetrachloride, decomposition to the more stable compound S_4N_3Cl takes place:

$$6S_3N_2Cl \rightarrow 4S_4N_3Cl + S_2Cl_2$$

The compound S_4N_3Cl can also be made by heating S_4N_4 with S_2Cl_2:

$$3S_4N_4 + 2S_2Cl_2 \rightarrow 4S_4N_3Cl$$

S_4N_3Cl is a bright yellow salt that dissolves in cold water to form a solution from which other salts may be precipitated by simple metathesis. Thus the compounds $(S_4N_3)NO_3$, $(S_4N_3)HSO_4$, $(S_4N_3)SCN$, $(S_4N_3)Br$, and $(S_4N_3)I$ have been prepared. X-ray diffraction studies have shown that the $S_4N_3^+$ cation has the structure

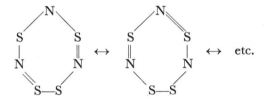

When S_4N_4 is treated with chlorine in chloroform or carbon tetrachloride, the yellow compound $S_3N_3Cl_3$ is formed:

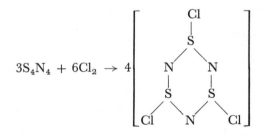

The latter compound forms an adduct with SO_3 which, on heating, yields SO_2 and sulfanuric trichloride:

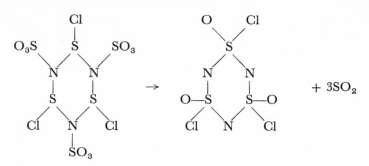

$S_3N_3Cl_3$ undergoes a remarkable reaction with $S_4N_4H_4$ in the presence of base to form S_4N_4:

$$4S_3N_3Cl_3 + 3S_4N_4H_4 + 12C_5H_5N \rightarrow 6S_4N_4 + 12C_5H_5N \cdot HCl$$

A large number of S—N—F compounds have been prepared, some of which are shown below:

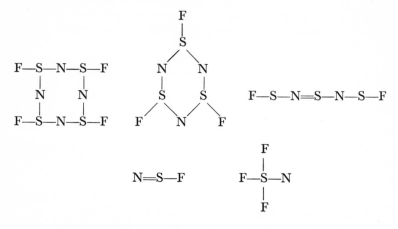

7-4 IMIDES AND AMIDES OF SULFUR OXY-ACIDS

Sulfurous Acid Derivatives

If we replace both hydroxyl groups of sulfurous acid (HO—SO—OH) with amido groups, we have thionyl amide. There have been some reported preparations of the latter compound, but they have not been verified, and it is possible that certain of these preparations actually involved the formation of the ammonium salt of HOSN, which is an isomer of $OS(NH_2)_2$.

If we replace one of the oxygen atoms of SO_2 with the imido group, we have thionyl imide, a compound which is much better characterized than thionyl amide. Five different isomers of thionyl imide, HNSO, have been reported. When ammonia and thionyl chloride are brought together in the gas phase at low temperatures, a volatile colorless material melting at about $-85°$ is formed:

$$3NH_3 + SOCl_2 \rightarrow H—N{=}S—O + 2NH_4Cl$$

At temperatures above $-60°$ this compound polymerizes to a brown polymer that probably has the structure

$$—NH—S—NH—S—$$
$$\quad\quad | \quad\quad\quad | $$
$$\quad\quad O \quad\quad\quad O$$

When the reaction between ammonia and thionyl chloride is carried out at room temperature in an organic solvent and in the presence of calcium oxide, a red solid compound of formula $HO—S{=}N$ forms. It is believed to have the indicated structure.

$$SOCl_2 + NH_3 + CaO \rightarrow HOSN + CaCl_2 + H_2O$$

This red compound readily polymerizes to the brown polymeric $(HNSO)_x$. A yellow crystalline isomer, of unknown degree of polymerization, may be prepared by the action of HCl on imido-sulfinamide, $NH_2SONHSONH_2$. This yellow isomer also is readily converted to the brown polymer. The fifth isomer, a solid red tetramer, is prepared by the oxidation of $S_4N_4H_4$ in air at 110 to 120°:

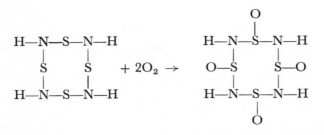

If we replace only one of the hydroxyl groups of sulfurous acid with an amido group, we have amidosulfurous acid, $HOSONH_2$. An ill-characterized product of this composition has been prepared by the reaction of ammonia with excess sulfur dioxide. It is not certain, however, that the material does not have the structure

Sulfuric Acid Derivatives

The reaction of sulfuryl chloride with excess ammonia yields, among other things, sulfuryl amide (also known as sulfamide).

$$SO_2Cl_2 + 4NH_3 \rightarrow SO_2(NH_2)_2 + 2NH_4Cl$$

Sulfamide is a white crystalline solid that melts at 93°.   Its aqueous solutions are only slightly acidic, but in liquid ammonia it is a strong dibasic acid.   When heated, sulfamide undergoes an exothermic reaction to an isomeric ammonium salt of empirical formula $NH_4(NSO_2)$.   This may be converted to a silver salt that in turn reacts with methyl iodide to yield

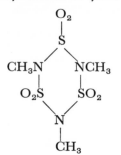

It is therefore possible that the ammonium salt is really a salt of the trimer of sulfimide, $(HNSO_2)_3$.

Amidosulfuric acid (or sulfamic acid) may be prepared by the reaction of sulfur trioxide with ammonia or by the reaction of urea with fuming sulfuric acid.

$$SO_3 + NH_3 \rightarrow SO_3NH_3$$

$$H_2SO_4 + SO_3 + CO(NH_2)_2 \rightarrow CO_2 + 2SO_3NH_3$$

X-ray studies show that solid sulfamic acid has a zwitterion structure,

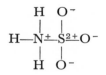

but it is usually assumed that, in aqueous solution, the molecular structure is $HOSO_2NH_2$, corresponding to a sulfuric acid molecule in which one of the hydroxyl groups has been replaced by an amido group. In aqueous solution the acid is quite strong $(K \sim 10^{-1})$, and the solid is often used as a primary standard in acidimetry.

REFERENCES

M. Goehring, *Ergebnisse und Probleme der Chemie der Schwefelstickstoffverbindungen*, Akademie-Verlag, Berlin, 1957.

M. Becke-Goehring, "Schwefel-stickstoff-verbindungen, *Progr. Inorg. Chem.*, **1** (**1959**), 207.

M. Becke-Goehring, "Amides and imides of the oxyacids of sulfur," *Advan. Inorg. Chem. Radiochem.*, **2**, 159 (1960).

M. Becke-Goehring, "Sechsgliedrige und achtgliedrige ringsysteme in der schwefel-chemie," *Angew Chem.*, **73**, 589 (1961).

L. F. Audrieth, M. Sveda, H. H. Sisler, and M. J. Butler, "Sulfamic acid, sulfamide, and related aquo-ammonosulfuric acids," *Chem. Rev.*, **26**, 49 (1940).

8

Phosphorus-Nitrogen
Compounds

8-1 PHOSPHORUS AMIDES AND NITRIDES

When ammonia is passed into a cold solution of a phosphorus
trihalide in an inert solvent, phosphorus triamide forms:

$$PCl_3 + 6NH_3 \rightarrow P(NH_2)_3 + 3NH_4Cl$$

Under similar conditions, ammonia and phosphorus pentachloride
form a material of empirical formula PN_3H_4:

$$PCl_5 + 8NH_3 \rightarrow 5NH_4Cl + PN_3H_4$$

The latter material is polymeric and is probably based on repeating
units of the type

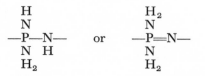

Both $P(NH_2)_3$ and PN_3H_4 lose ammonia, hydrogen, or nitrogen stepwise to eventually form the polymer $(PN)_x$:

$$P(NH_2)_3 \rightarrow P_2(NH)_3 \rightarrow P_2N_3$$

$$(PN)_x$$

$$PN_3H_4 \rightarrow PN_2H \rightarrow P_3N_5$$

Solid phosphorus nitrides having N:P ratios between 0.9 and 1.7 can be prepared by the reaction of phosphorus and nitrogen in an electric arc, in a silent electric discharge, or at a hot tungsten filament.

The low-temperature reaction of phosphorus trichloride with excess methylamine yields the remarkable compound phosphorus tri-N-methylimide, $P_4N_6(CH_3)_6$. It is very likely that this material has a structure analogous to that of P_4O_6, in which phosphorus atoms in a tetrahedral distribution are joined by N—CH$_3$ groups:

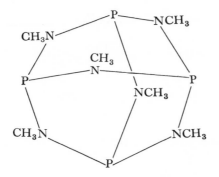

The analogous compound, $P_2(NH)_3$, may have a similar structure.

8-2 AMIDO DERIVATIVES OF PHOSPHORIC ACID

Phosphoryl triamide, $PO(NH_2)_3$, may be prepared by slowly adding a cold solution of $POCl_3$ in chloroform to a cold solution of ammonia in the same solvent:

$$POCl_3 + 6NH_3 \rightarrow PO(NH_2)_3 + 3NH_4Cl$$

Phosphoryl triamide is a white solid that is insoluble in most organic solvents and is only slightly soluble in water. When warmed with aqueous base, the amide forms the diamidophosphate ion:

$$PO(NH_2)_3 + OH^- \rightarrow OPO(NH_2)_2^- + NH_3$$

The corresponding acid, diamidophosphoric acid, is a weak acid in aqueous solution ($pK \sim 4.6$) and may be precipitated by the addition of cold glacial acetic acid.

Another way for preparing diamidophosphates or diamidophosphoric acid is through the formation of phenyl dichlorophosphate followed by its ammonolysis and saponification:

$$POCl_3 \xrightarrow{C_6H_5OH} C_6H_5OPOCl_2 \xrightarrow{NH_3} C_6H_5OPO(NH_2)_2$$
$$\downarrow OH^-$$
$$HOPO(NH_2)_2 \xleftarrow[H^+]{} OPO(NH_2)_2^-$$

In a similar way, monoamidophosphates may be prepared:

$$POCl_3 \xrightarrow{C_6H_5OH} (C_6H_5O)_2POCl \xrightarrow{NH_3} (C_6H_5O)_2PO(NH_2)$$
$$\downarrow KOH$$
$$(HO)_2PO(NH_2) \xleftarrow[ClO_4^-]{H^+} KHPO_3(NH_2)$$

Monoamidophosphoric acid is a dibasic acid with $pK_1 \sim 2.8$ and $pK_2 \sim 8.2$.

When disodium monoamidophosphate is heated to 210° in vacuo, one obtains tetrasodium imidodiphosphate the anionic structure of which is:

$$\left[\begin{matrix} O & H & O \\ OP-N-PO \\ O & & O \end{matrix} \right]^{4-}$$

Heating to 450° yields the nitridotriphosphate:

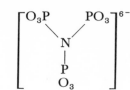

8-3 PHOSPHONITRILIC COMPOUNDS

When phosphorus pentachloride and ammonium chloride are heated together, a series of compounds with the general formula $(PNCl_2)_n$ is formed:

$$PCl_5 + NH_4Cl \rightarrow \frac{1}{n}(PNCl_2)_n + 4HCl$$

These compounds are usually called phosphonitrilic chlorides; pure compounds have been isolated only for values of n from 3 to 8, although higher members of the series, including a rubber-like polymer, exist. The trimeric phosphonitrilic chloride melts at 114° and boils at 256.5°. The structure is as shown below, the P_3N_3 ring being planar with equivalent (at least almost equivalent) P—N bonds. Undoubtedly there is some use of the phosphorus $3d$

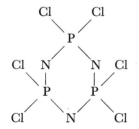

orbitals in the bonding, and so the P—N bonds have some double-bond character. The tetrameric phosphonitrilic chloride melts at 124° and boils at 328.5°. The molecule consists of an eight-membered ring of alternating P and N atoms, with two Cl atoms attached to each phosphorus atom. The P—N bonds are equivalent, and the ring is shaped like the boat form of cycloöctatetraene.

Potassium fluorosulfite, KSO_2F, reacts with the phosphonitrilic chlorides to form the corresponding phosphonitrilic fluorides, $(PNF_2)_n$. By fractional distillation and gas chromatography, members of this series have been separated up to $n = 17$.

The hydrolysis of an ether solution of $(PNCl_2)_3$ with aqueous acetate gives the trimetaphosphimate anion:

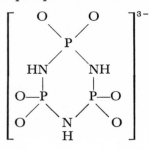

Ammonolysis of $(PNCl_2)_3$ has yielded the diamino derivative, $P_3N_3Cl_4(NH_2)_2$, and the hexamino derivative, $P_3N_3(NH_2)_6$. Aminolysis yields similar products.

REFERENCES

J. R. Van Wazer, *Phosphorus and Its Compounds*, Vol. I, pp. 309–332, 830–843, Interscience, New York, 1958.

N. L. Paddock and H. T. Searle, "Phosphonitrilic compounds," *Advan. Inorg. Chem. Radiochem.*, **1**, 347 (1959).

R. A. Shaw, B. W. Fitzsimmons, and B. C. Smith, "Phosphonitrilic compounds," *Chem. Rev.*, **62**, 247 (1962).

C. P. Haber, "Phosphonitrilic compounds," in "Inorganic polymers," *Chem. Soc. (London) Spec. Publ.* 15 (1961), 115.

9

Carbon-Nitrogen Compounds

9-1 CYANOGEN, $(CN)_2$

Cyanogen is the best known of the so-called pseudohalogens or halogenoids. Its chemistry closely resembles that of the halogens, particularly iodine. The preparative methods for cyanogen (heating a noble-metal cyanide and oxidation of cyanide by cupric ion) are analogous to reactions in which iodine is liberated:

$$2AuCN \rightarrow 2Au + (CN)_2$$
$$2Cu^{2+} + 4CN^- \rightarrow 2CuCN + (CN)_2$$

Cyanogen is a colorless, poisonous gas with a distinctive odor. Its melting and boiling points are $-27.9°$ and $-21.2°$, respectively. Molecular cyanogen is linear, with the structure $N{\equiv}C{-}C{\equiv}N$. When heated to 400 to 500°, cyanogen polymerizes to a white, insoluble solid, paracyanogen, $(CN)_x$.

In alkaline solution, cyanogen disproportionates to cyanide and cyanate:

$$(CN)_2 + 2OH^- \rightarrow CN^- + CNO^- + H_2O$$

Although the disproportionation is thermodynamically possible in both acid and alkaline solutions, the rate is appreciable only in alkaline solutions.

9-2 CYANIDE, CN⁻, AND HYDROGEN CYANIDE, HCN

Sodium cyanide may be made by the reaction of sodium amide with carbon at red heat,

$$NaNH_2 + C \rightarrow H_2 + NaCN$$

or by the fusion of calcium cyanamide and carbon with sodium carbonate,

$$CaCN_2 + C + Na_2CO_3 \rightarrow CaCO_3 + 2NaCN$$

The cyanide ion is isoelectronic with molecular nitrogen: $:C{\equiv}N:$. Like the corresponding iodides, AgCN, $Hg_2(CN)_2$, and $Pb(CN)_2$ are very insoluble. Aqueous solutions of cyanide are alkaline because of extensive hydrolysis to form the weak acid HCN ($K_a = 4 \times 10^{-10}$):

$$CN^- + H_2O = HCN + OH^-$$

Anhydrous HCN is a liquid (bp 25.6°) of high dielectric constant ($\epsilon = 107$ at 25°) that, in spite of its extremely poisonous nature, is used as a nonaqueous solvent. The gas has the odor of bitter almonds; it causes death from short exposure to concentrations as low as 2 mg/liter. Hydrogen cyanide is very soluble in water. In the absence of stabilizers, HCN can polymerize to form, among other polymers, a tetramer $(HCN)_4$. In the crystal the carbon-nitrogen skeleton is planar.

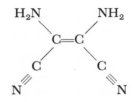

9-3 CYANATE, OCN⁻

Cyanates are prepared by the action of mild oxidizing agents on cyanides. Thus, lead oxide and the tetrammine copper(II) ion can serve this purpose:

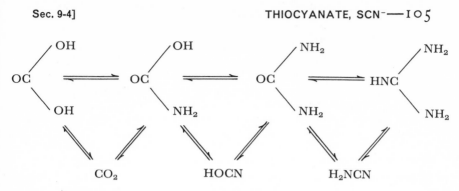

Figure 9-1 *The aquo-ammono carbonic acids.*

$$PbO + KCN \rightarrow KOCN + Pb$$

$$2Cu(NH_3)_4^{2+} + 3CN^- + 2OH^- \rightarrow$$
$$2CuCN + OCN^- + 8NH_3 + H_2O$$

Cyanic acid is moderately weak:

$$HOCN = H^+ + OCN^- \qquad K = 1.2 \times 10^{-4}$$

The free acid decomposes in aqueous solution to carbonic acid and ammonia.

$$HOCN + 2H_2O \rightarrow H_2CO_3 + NH_3$$

Cyanic acid may be looked upon as an aquo-ammono carbonic acid.   By reference to Figure 9-1 it can be seen that cyanic acid is the dehydration product of carbamic acid and the deammonation product of urea.   Indeed, when the alkali metal salts of carbamic acid or urea are heated, the corresponding cyanates are formed.

The cyanate ion has the structure $O\!=\!C\!=\!N \leftrightarrow O\!-\!C\!\equiv\!N$. The ion is linear and, in the sodium salt, has the dimensions $O\!-\!C \sim 1.13$ Å and $C\!-\!N \sim 1.21$ Å.   The free acid has the iso configuration, $H\!-\!N\!=\!C\!=\!O$, with $H\!-\!N$ 0.987 Å, $N\!-\!C$ 1.21 Å, and $C\!-\!O$ 1.17 Å.

9-4 THIOCYANATE, SCN⁻

Thiocyanates are prepared by the reaction of sulfur with cyanides in the fused state:

$$KCN + S \rightarrow KSCN$$

Like the cyanate ion, the thiocyanate ion is linear with the carbon atom in the middle. The free acid has the iso configuration, HNCS.

The aqueous thiocyanate ion is readily oxidized to thio-cyanogen, $(SCN)_2$:

$$2SCN^- = (SCN)_2 + 2e^- \qquad E^\circ = -0.77 \text{ volt}$$

From the oxidation potential we see that thiocyanogen lies between bromine and iodine in its oxidizing power. On standing, thio-cyanogen polymerizes to brick-red parathiocyanogen, $(SCN)_x$, the structure of which is unknown.

9-5 CYANAMIDE AND ITS ISOMERS

Calcium carbide reacts with nitrogen at about 1000° to form the calcium salt of cyanamide:

$$CaC_2 + N_2 \rightarrow CaCN_2 + C$$

The cyanamide ion is isoelectronic with the CO_2 molecule: $^-N{=}C{=}N^-$. Aqueous acid converts calcium cyanamide to cyanamide, $H_2N{-}C{\equiv}N$, a solid that melts at 46° and is very soluble in water, alcohol, and ether.

$$CaCN_2 + 2H^+ \rightarrow Ca^{2+} + H_2NCN$$

In alkaline solution, cyanamide dimerizes to form dicyandiamide, otherwise known as cyanoguanidine:

$$2H_2NCN \rightarrow \overset{\displaystyle NH}{\overset{\|}{N{\equiv}C{-}NH{-}C{-}NH_2}}$$

At elevated temperatures, dicyandiamide polymerizes to form melamine, or cyanuric amide.

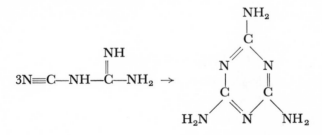

It will be noted from Figure 9-1 that cyanamide may be thought of as the dehydration product of urea and as the deammonation product of guanidine.   These relationships are more than formal. Thus, urea may be obtained from the hydrolysis of calcium cyanamide, and guanidine salts may be obtained by heating cyanamide with ammonium salts.

Diazomethane, $H_2C{=}N{=}N$, is an isomer of cyanamide, but it is not chemically similar to cyanamide.   Diazomethane is prepared by the treatment of N-nitrosomethylurea with concentrated aqueous alkali:

$$\overset{\displaystyle NO}{\underset{\displaystyle |}{CH_3{-}N}}{-}(CO){-}NH_2 + OH^- \rightarrow CH_2N_2 + CNO^- + 2H_2O$$

It is a yellow, poisonous, explosive gas with a boiling point of $-24°$. It is usually used in ether solution.   Diazomethane is an important methylating agent.   Thus halogen compounds may be converted to the corresponding halomethyl compounds, and certain hydrides may be converted to the corresponding methyl compounds.

$$GeCl_4 + CH_2N_2 \rightarrow ClCH_2GeCl_3 + N_2$$

$$R_3SnH + CH_2N_2 \rightarrow R_3SnCH_3 + N_2$$

Isodiazomethane is believed to have the structure

$$HC{\equiv}N{-}NH \leftrightarrow HC{=}N{=}NH$$

It has been prepared by forming a salt of diazomethane,

$$CH_2N_2 + LiCH_3 \rightarrow LiCHN_2 + CH_4$$

followed by careful acidification of the salt:

$$LiCHN_2 + NH_4^+ \rightarrow Li^+ + NH_3 + HCN_2H$$

Isodiazomethane is moderately stable in ether solution, but the yellowish liquid that is obtained upon evaporation of the ether decomposes at room temperature.   The compound readily isomerizes to diazomethane upon treatment with potassium hydroxide.

A fourth isomer, cyclodiazomethane, or diazirine, is believed to have the structure

This compound has been prepared by the oxidation of the corresponding hydro compound and by the reaction of difluoramine with azomethines.

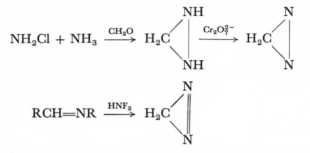

Cyclodiazomethane is a colorless, explosive gas of boiling point −14°. The compound is less reactive than diazomethane. It reacts only slowly with sulfuric acid, and it is unaffected by strong bases such as the *t*-butoxide ion.

REFERENCES

F. C. Whitmore, *Organic Chemistry*, 2d ed., Vol. I, Dover, New York, 1951.
L. F. Audrieth and J. Kleinberg, *Non-Aqueous Solvents*, Chap. 4 (The nitrogen system of compounds), Wiley, New York, 1953.

IO

Boron-Nitrogen Compounds

10-1 BORON NITRIDE, BN

Boron nitride is the ultimate product of pyrolysis of a large number of boron-nitrogen compounds, including $B_3N_3H_6$, $B(NH_2)_3$, $BF_3 \cdot NH_3$, $B_2H_6 \cdot 2NH_3$, and mixtures of B_2O_3 and NH_4Cl. It is a white, slippery solid of density 2.25 g/cc. It is a refractory and relatively chemically inert material. Boron nitride is unaffected by aqueous acids or alkalies, but it is hydrolyzed at red heat by water vapor.

Boron nitride that has been prepared as described above has an hexagonal crystal structure. The material consists of parallel planes of hexagonal rings of alternating boron and nitrogen atoms:

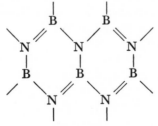

A boron-nitrogen bond is isoelectronic with a carbon-carbon bond, and one is struck by the superficial resemblance of the hexagonal boron nitride structure to that of graphite. There are significant differences in the properties and structures of these materials, however. Boron nitride is not as good an electrical conductor as graphite. Apparently the π electrons in boron nitride are somewhat localized on the nitrogen atoms, but there is some delocalization of the π electrons with consequent polarity of the B—N bonds. This polarity is the cause of a fundamental difference in the structures of BN and graphite. In graphite, the planes are stacked in such a way that half of the carbon atoms are on lines through the ring centers of the adjacent planes. In boron nitride, the hexagons are lined up with those in adjacent planes, with each nitrogen atom at the middle of a perpendicular line between boron atoms in the two adjacent planes.

When ordinary hexagonal boron nitride is subjected to a pressure of at least 45,000 atm at 1500° or higher, it is converted (in the presence of catalysts such as alkali and alkaline-earth metals or their nitrides) to a cubic form analogous to that of diamond. The cubic form of boron nitride has a density of 3.47 g/cc; it is hard enough to scratch diamond; and it is quite inert chemically.

10-2 THE REACTION OF BORON HALIDES WITH AMMONIA AND AMINES

The trihalides of boron, except BF_3, react with excess ammonia at temperatures at about $-50°$ to form boron triamide:

$$BX_3 + 6NH_3 \rightarrow B(NH_2)_3 + 3NH_4X$$

The amide slowly loses ammonia at temperatures greater than 0° to form $B_2(NH)_3$, although the deammonation is best carried out at 100°. At temperatures above 200°, decomposition to BN occurs.

Boron trifluoride reacts with ammonia to form the very stable coordination compound F_3B—NH_3. This ammoniate is a crystalline solid with a density of 1.86 and a melting point of 163°. It dissolves in both water and liquid ammonia with little solvolysis.

Secondary amines react with BCl_3 and BBr_3 to form tris-(dialkylamino)boranes, $B(NR_2)_3$. Partially aminolyzed boron halides of the type $XB(NR_2)_2$ have also been prepared. In fact, these compounds may be prepared by reaction of $B(NR_2)_3$ with the appropriate boron trihalide:

$$2B(NR_2)_3 + BX_3 \rightarrow 3XB(NR_2)_2$$

Chloro-bis(dimethylamino)borane undergoes an interesting reaction with highly dispersed molten sodium to form tetra(dimethylamino)diboron.   This reaction offers a convenient route to com-

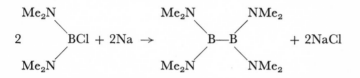

pounds containing boron-boron bonds.

Tertiary amines such as trimethylamine and pyridine form stable coordination compounds of the type $BX_3 \cdot NR_3$ with the boron halides.

10-3   BORANE AMMONIATES

Boron alkyls (alkyl boranes) are Lewis acids and form stable 1:1 coordination compounds with ammonia.   Typically, these compounds are colorless, volatile compounds that may be readily sublimed at room temperature in vacuo.

Ammonia-borane, H_3NBH_3, may be prepared by the reaction of ammonia with dimethyl ether-borane,

$$(CH_3)_2OBH_3 + NH_3 \rightarrow H_3NBH_3 + (CH_3)_2O$$

or by the reaction of an alkali borohydride with an ammonium salt in ether,

$$LiBH_4 + NH_4Cl \rightarrow LiCl + H_3NBH_3 + H_2$$

Ammonia-borane is a monomeric compound which is slightly volatile at room temperature.   In liquid ammonia, it reacts with sodium to form one equivalent of hydrogen per mole of ammonia-borane:

$$H_3NBH_3 + e^- \rightarrow \tfrac{1}{2}H_2 + H_3BNH_2^-$$

Diborane reacts at low temperatures with ammonia to form a "diammoniate," $B_2H_6 \cdot 2NH_3$, which is distinctly different from the compound H_3NBH_3. The "diammoniate" is a nonvolatile, salt-like compound that is believed to have the structure

$$\left[\begin{array}{c} H \\ | \\ H_3N\!-\!B\!-\!NH_3 \\ | \\ H \end{array} \right]^+ BH_4^-$$

Chemical evidence for the borohydride ion has been obtained in the reactions of ammonium halides with the diammoniate:

$$[H_2B(NH_3)_2]BH_4 + 2NH_4X \rightarrow 2[H_2B(NH_3)_2]X + 2H_2$$

Alkali-metal borohydrides react with ammonium halides to form $[H_2B(NH_3)_2]X$ salts:

$$MBH_4 + 2NH_4X \rightarrow MX + [H_2B(NH_3)_2]X + 2H_2$$

10-4 BORANE-AMINE COORDINATION COMPOUNDS

Addition compounds of the type $BR_3 \cdot NR_3$, $BR_3 \cdot NHR_2$, and $BR_3 \cdot NH_2R$ are readily prepared by the reaction of the appropriate alkyl boranes and amines. Diborane reacts with amines to form borane-amine coordination compounds:

$$\tfrac{1}{2}B_2H_6 + NR_3 \rightarrow H_3BNR_3$$
$$\tfrac{1}{2}B_2H_6 + NHR_2 \rightarrow H_3BNHR_2$$

Similar compounds are formed by using alkyl diboranes:

$$\tfrac{1}{2}B_2H_4R_2 + NR_3 \rightarrow R_3NBH_2R$$

These compounds have considerable thermal stability when the amine is tertiary. Thus $(CH_3)_3NBH_3$ and $(CH_3)_3NBH_2CH_3$ are stable toward prolonged heating at $100°$. However, when there are hydrogen atoms on both the nitrogen and boron atoms, the compounds lose hydrogen when heated to form *borazenes*:

$$2(CH_3)_2HNBH_3 \rightarrow \begin{array}{c} (CH_3)_2N\!-\!\!-\!\!-BH_2 \\ | \quad\quad | \\ H_2B\!-\!\!-\!\!-N(CH_3)_2 \end{array} + 2H_2$$

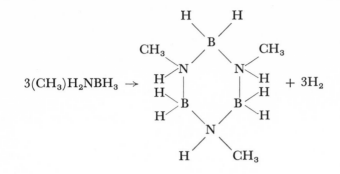

$$3(CH_3)H_2NBH_3 \rightarrow \quad + 3H_2$$

10-5 BORAZINE

When a mixture of lithium borohydride and ammonium chloride is heated to 230 to 300°, borazine (the boron-nitrogen analog of benzene) is formed:

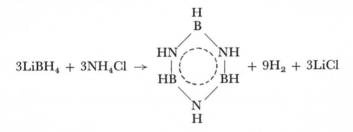

$$3LiBH_4 + 3NH_4Cl \rightarrow \quad + 9H_2 + 3LiCl$$

Borazine is a colorless liquid of density 0.86 g/cc that freezes at −58° and boils at 55°. As might be expected, it has a planar structure similar to that of benzene.

Unlike benzene, borazine very readily forms adducts of the type $B_3N_3H_6 \cdot 3HX$ with hydrogen halides. The latter compounds are believed to have cyclohexane-like structures. The hydrochloride of borazine may be reduced to form hexahydroborazine.

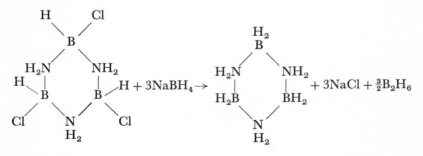

$$+ 3NaBH_4 \rightarrow \quad + 3NaCl + \tfrac{3}{2}B_2H_6$$

REFERENCES

R. H. Wentorf, Jr., " Synthesis of the cubic form of boron nitride," *J. Chem. Phys.*, **34**, 809 (1961).

A. B. Burg, "Bonding in boron compounds and in inorganic polymers," *J. Chem. Educ.*, **37**, 482 (1960).

W. Gerrard, *The Organic Chemistry of Boron*, Academic, New York, 1961.

G. E. Coates, *Organo-Metallic Compounds*, 2d ed., Wiley, New York, 1960.

G. H. Dahl and R. Schaeffer, " Preparation and properties of hexahydroborazine," *J. Am. Chem. Soc.*, **83**, 3032 (1961).

I I

Thermodynamics of Nitrogen Compounds

11-1 THERMODYNAMIC FUNCTIONS AT 25°

The heats of formation, free energies of formation, and entropies for some important nitrogen-containing species are presented in Table 11-1. By combining these functions with similar functions that are tabulated in Latimer's *Oxidation Potentials* and the *National Bureau of Standards Circular 500* (see References), one may calculate thermodynamic data at 25° for an enormous number of reactions.

One is struck by the fact that most of the free energies of formation in Table 11-1 are positive. This indicates that most nitrogen compounds are unstable with respect to their elements and emphasizes the fact that, in nitrogen chemistry, thermodynamically favored reactions often proceed at a negligible rate. In this connection, it is interesting to look at the heats of formation of the trans and cis isomers of N_2F_2. From the data we calculate $\Delta H° = -3.0$ kcal/mole for the isomerization

$$N_2F_2(trans) \rightarrow N_2F_2(cis)$$

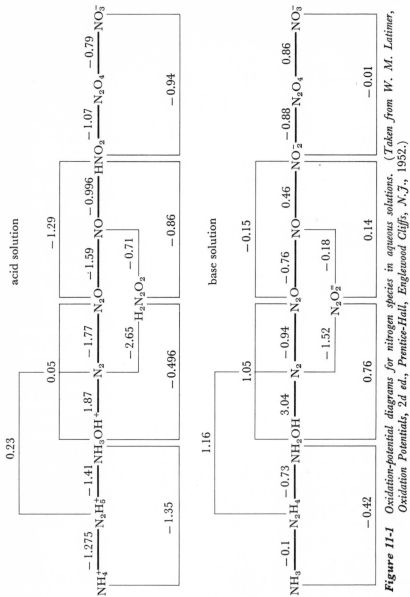

Figure 11-1 Oxidation-potential diagrams for nitrogen species in aqueous solutions. (*Taken from W. M. Latimer, Oxidation Potentials, 2d ed., Prentice-Hall, Englewood Cliffs, N.J., 1952.*)

Table 11-1   *Thermodynamic functions at 25° for some nitrogen species*

Species	State	ΔH_f°, kcal/mole	ΔF_f°, kcal/mole	S°, cal/mole-deg
N	g	113.00	108.76	36.61
N$^+$	g	448.46		
N^{2+}	g	1131.21		
N$_2$	g	0	0	45.767
N$_3^-$	aq	60.3	77.7	32 ?
NO	g	21.60	20.72	50.339
NO$_2$	g	8.09	12.39	57.47
NO$_2^-$	aq	−25.4	−8.25	29.9
NO$_3$	g	16.95	27.36	60.36
NO$_3^-$	aq	−49.37	−26.43	35.0
N$_2$O	g	19.49	24.76	52.58
N$_2$O$_2^{2-}$	aq	−2.59	33.2	6.6
N$_2$O$_3$	g	20.00	33.49	73.92
N$_2$O$_4$	g	2.54	23.66	72.73
N$_2$O$_5$	c	−10.0	32	27
N$_2$O$_5$	g	3.35	28.18	85.00
NH	g	84		
NH$_2$	g	41		
NH$_3$	g	−11.04	−3.976	46.01
NH$_3$	aq	−19.32	−6.36	26.3
NH$_4^+$	g	154		44.47
NH$_4^+$	aq	−31.74	−19.00	26.97
N$_2$H$_2$	g	48.7		
N$_2$H$_4$	g	22.7		
N$_2$H$_4$	l	12.0	35.61	
HN$_3$	g	70.3	78.5	56.7
HNO$_2$	aq	−28.4	−12.82	
HNO$_3$	g	−31.99		63.62
HNO$_3$	l	−41.40	−19.10	37.19
NH$_2$OH	g	−14.7		
NH$_2$OH	c	−25.5		
NH$_2$OH	aq	−21.7	−5.60	40
HN$_2$O$_2^-$	aq	−9.4	18.2	34
H$_2$N$_2$O$_2$	aq	−13.7	8.6	52
NF$_3$	g	−29.7	−19.7	62.25
N$_2$F$_2$(*trans*)	g	19.4		
N$_2$F$_2$(*cis*)	g	16.4		
NOF	g	−15.8		
NOCl	g	12.57	15.86	63.0
NOBr	g	19.56	19.70	65.16
S$_4$N$_4$	c	127.6		

ΔS° is probably very close to zero for this reaction, and so we conclude that the cis form is thermodynamically stable with respect to the trans form. However, we have pointed out in Chapter 4 that the cis form is much more reactive than the trans form. Thus again we have proof that reactivity is not always predictable from thermodynamics.

Since nitrogen exhibits a large number of oxidation states (-3 to $+5$) in its compounds, it is helpful to summarize free energy data for nitrogen compounds by means of oxidation-potential diagrams. In Figure 11-1, such diagrams are presented for the more important nitrogen species that exist in aqueous solutions. It will be noted that, in both acidic and basic solutions, all the species with oxidation states between -3 and $+5$ are unstable with respect to disproportionation to molecular nitrogen and either ammonia or nitrate ion.

All nitrogen compounds potentially are good reducing agents with respect to oxidation to N_2 or are good oxidizing agents with respect to reduction to N_2. Only in the case of hydrazine, however, is it possible to go quantitatively to N_2. There is probably no connection between this fact and the fact that the two nitrogen atoms of hydrazine are already bonded together. In hyponitrous acid the two nitrogen atoms are bonded together (in fact, by a double bond), yet reduction to N_2 does not occur.

11-2 BOND ENERGIES AND DISSOCIATION ENERGIES

The difference between bond energies and dissociation energies can be made clear by discussing the molecules ammonia and hydrazine. The atomization of ammonia gas,

$$NH_3(g) = N(g) + 3H(g)$$

is endothermic to the extent of 280.3 kcal/mole at 25°. In this reaction, three N—H bonds are broken, and by convention we take one-third of the heat of atomization, or 93.4 kcal/mole, as the N—H *bond energy*, $E(N—H)$. It must not be assumed that, when the hydrogen atoms of ammonia are removed stepwise, each step involves the absorption of 93.4 kcal/mole. It happens that the energy for each of these steps has been measured. These *dissociation energies* are listed below.

$$D(NH_2—H) = 104 \text{ kcal/mole}$$
$$D(NH—H) = 95 \text{ kcal/mole}$$
$$D(N—H) = 81 \text{ kcal/mole}$$

Table 11-2 *Bond energies for nitrogen-oxygen and nitrogen-nitrogen bonds*

Bond	Bond order	Typical molecule	Bond energy, kcal/mole, 25°C
N̈—O	1	NH_2OH	46
N⁺—O	1	$HONO_2$	57
⁺½ N∸∸O ⁻⅙	1.33	NO_3	91
⁺ N∸∸O ⁻½	1.5	CH_3NO_2	103
⁺½ N∸∸O ⁻¼	1.75	NO_2	112
N̈=O	2	HONO	146
N⁺=O	2	NO_2^+	159[a]
⁻½ N∸∸O ⁺½	2.5	NO	151
:N≡O⁺	3	NO^+	264[a]
N̈—N̈	1	N_2H_4	38
N̈—N⁺	1	NH_2NO_2	67
N⁺—N⁺	1	N_2O_4	52
N̈=N̈	2	N_2H_2	99
⁺½ N∸∸N ⁺½	2.5	N_2^+	202
:N≡N:	3	N_2	226

[a] Calculated by apportioning the charge equally among the dissociated atoms.

It will be noted that the average of these dissociation energies is equal to $E(N—H)$. It is interesting to conjecture as to the reason for the regular decrease in dissociation energy in the series $D(NH_2—H)$, $D(NH—H)$, $D(N—H)$. Perhaps this trend is attributable to an increasing degree of p character in the bonds as the number of nonbonding electrons increases. The nonbonding electrons prefer to occupy the nitrogen-atom s orbital so as to minimize their energy, and, as the s character of the bonding orbitals decreases, the bond energies decrease.

The heat of atomization of hydrazine, N_2H_4, is 411.6 kcal/ mole. By assuming that the bond energy of the N—H bonds is

Table 11-3 *Dissociation energies of isoelectronic species*

Species	D, kcal/ mole	Species	D, kcal/ mole	Species	D, kcal/ mole
N≡N	226	HN=NH	119	H_2N—NH_2	60
HC≡N	224	HN=O	119	H_2N—OH	66
HC≡CH	228	O=O	118	HO—OH	52

the same as in ammonia, we calculate $411.6 - 4 \times 93.4 = 38.0$ kcal/mole for the N—N bond energy in hydrazine. This bond energy is distinctly different from the N—N bond dissociation energy, $D(NH_2$—$NH_2) = 60$ kcal/mole:

$$N_2H_4 \rightarrow 2NH_2$$

This dissociation has been discussed in Section 5-3 under the subheading The Amide Radical.

Nitrogen forms a remarkable variety of compounds containing nitrogen-oxygen bonds in which the N—O bond order ranges from 1, as in hydroxylamine, to 3, as in nitrosyl salts. In Table 11-2 the bond energies calculated from a series of such compounds are arranged in the order of increasing bond order. A similar, but shorter, series of N—N bond energies is also presented. It is clear that the bond energies increase in a fairly regular way with increasing bond order. In fact, it is possible to make rough estimates of unknown N—O and N—N bond energies by using Table 11-2.

It is interesting to compare the dissociation energies $D(N≡N)$, $D(HN=NH)$, and $D(NH_2$—$NH_2)$ with the corresponding dissociation energies for molecules that are isoelectronic with each of these. This comparison is made in Table 11-3, where these dissociation energies have been tabulated. It can be seen that the dissociation energies for isoelectronic species are of very similar magnitude.

REFERENCES

"Selected values of chemical thermodynamic constants," *Natl. Bur. Standards Circ. 500*, 1952.

W. M. Latimer, *Oxidation Potentials*, 2d ed., Prentice-Hall, Englewood Cliffs, N.J., 1952.

Index